WORLDS WITHIN WORLDS:
THE STORY OF NUCLEAR ENERGY

ISAAC ASIMOV

FOREWORD BY JAMES HOLAHAN

UNIVERSITY PRESS OF THE PACIFIC INC.
SEATTLE, WASHINGTON

Distributed by.
International Scholarly Book Services, Inc.
2130 Pacific Avenue
Forest Grove, Oregon 97116

TABLE OF CONTENTS

FOREWORD
James Holahan

In the last 20 years, Isaac Asimov has written more than 150 books, including science fiction and many technical guides to scientific subjects. His prodigious output has made him one of America's favorite interpreters of the roles of science and technology in shaping man's destiny.

In this volume, Asimov explains scientific concepts of nuclear reactions in terms that make this incredible source of energy understandable to lay persons.

Asimov gives meaning to atoms, electrons, neutrons, and protons, and he explains the structure of the nucleus. An understanding of nuclear structure was the key that opened the world of nuclear energy to mankind. Nuclear energy has been working for mankind for billions of years. The sun, for example, is a nuclear power plant, the primary source of energy. Before man could duplicate the natural process going on in the sun, he had to understand the atom.

The roles of the atom and electricity are bound together, so it is not surprising that even in the late 1800's men dreamed of using these infinitesimally small building blocks of nature to create a limitless supply of inexpensive energy. A major breakthrough came with the invention of the vacuum tube, which demonstrated the working relationship between atoms and electrons and led to the discovery of radioactivity.

By this time, the relative atomic weights of various elements had been worked out. It was found that uranium, with the highest atomic weight of then known elements, was an endless source of radiation. With this discovery, scientists stood at the threshold of new knowledge that would affect the future of mankind.

The constant digging by scientists into the unknown has turned up data and information that has led to changes affecting the lives of everyone. Heating with solar energy has arrived, and this energy source has been approved for agricultural grain drying. Experiments in weather modification through cloud seeding are promising. The search for knowledge continues.

The next frontier in nuclear energy is controlled nuclear fusion. Asimov explains how to differentiate this process from nuclear fission. ". . . Mass for mass," he says, "nuclear fusion would produce far more energy than nuclear fission." To formulate this rule, scientists had to understand what was going on within the sun in order to duplicate conditions in which ". . . . bare nuclei, smashing together at central-sun temperatures could cling together and form more complex nuclei."

Nuclear reactions brought about by millions of degrees of heat are called *thermonuclear reactions*. The thermonuclear reactions of the sun, Asimov points out, have been going on for the last five billion years, and the sun will continue to radiate energy in the present fashion for at least five billion more.

An essential element for nuclear fusion is deuterium, an isotope of hydrogen, which is present in the ocean. Asimov says, "The deuterium in the world's ocean, if allowed to undergo gradual fusion, would supply mankind with enough to keep us going at the present rate for 500 billion years . . . for as long as mankind will exist."

Where will science lead? Who knows? The more man discovers, the more he wonders; when he wonders, he must continue searching. New worlds of scientific knowledge have been found inside the invisible atom, but new frontiers for research have been found in far larger entities, such as the ocean and space. Awareness of these new frontiers has created eagerness to join the struggle for new knowledge.

Science has imitated and almost outstripped science fiction. Man has walked on the moon, following procedures described by Jules Verne. Man has not found the way to travel at the speed of light, but that does not mean he will not. It only means he has not.

Asimov is a historian, chronicler, and prophet. The story he tells is exciting, optimistic, and vital to mankind.

James Holahan is vice president of Minerva Consulting Group, New York City. He is a writer on science subjects, and a member of various professional scientific societies.

1

ATOMIC WEIGHTS

As long ago as ancient Greek times, there were men who suspected that all matter consisted of tiny particles which were far too small to see. Under ordinary circumstances, they could not be divided into anything smaller, and they were called *atoms* from a Greek word meaning *indivisible*.

It was not until 1808, however, that this *atomic theory* was really put on a firm foundation. In that year the English chemist John Dalton published a book in which he discussed atoms in detail. Every element, he suggested, was made up of its own type of atoms. The atoms of one element were different from the atoms of every other element. The chief difference between the various atoms lay in their mass, or weight.*

Dalton was the first to try to determine what these masses might be. He could not work out the actual masses in ounces or grams, for atoms were far too tiny to weigh with any of his instruments. He could, however, determine their relative weights; that is, how much more massive one kind of atom might be than another.

For instance, he found that a quantity of hydrogen gas invariably combined with eight times its own mass of oxygen gas to form water. He guessed that water consisted of combinations of 1 atom of hydrogen with 1 atom of oxygen. (A combination of atoms is called a *molecule* from a Greek word meaning *a small mass,* and so hydrogen and oxygen atoms can be said to combine to form a *water molecule.*)

To account for the difference in the masses of the combining gases, Dalton decided that the oxygen atom was eight times as massive as the hydrogen atom. If he set the mass of the hydrogen atom at 1 (just for convenience) then the mass of the oxygen atom ought to be set at 8. These comparative, or relative, numbers were said to be *atomic weights,* so that what Dalton was suggesting was that the atomic weight of hydrogen was 1 and the atomic weight of oxygen was 8. By noting the quantity of other elements that combined with a fixed mass of oxygen or of hydrogen, Dalton could work out the atomic weights of these elements as well.

Dalton's idea was right, but his details were wrong in some cases. For instance, on closer examination it turned out that the water molecule was composed of 1 oxygen atom and 2 hydrogen atoms. For this reason, the water molecule may be written H_2O, where H is the chemical symbol for a hydrogen atom, and O for an oxygen atom.

It is still a fact that a quantity of hydrogen combines with eight times its mass of oxygen, so the single oxygen atom must be eight times as massive as the 2 hydrogen atoms taken together. The oxygen atom must therefore be sixteen times as massive as a single hydrogen atom. If the atomic weight of hydrogen is 1, then the atomic weight of oxygen is 16.

At first it seemed that the atomic weights of the various elements were whole numbers and that hydrogen was the lightest one. It made particular sense, then, to consider the atomic weight of hydrogen as 1, because that made all the other atomic weights as small as possible and therefore easy to handle.

The Swedish chemist Jöns Jakob Berzelius continued Dalton's work and found that elements did not combine in quite such simple ratios. A given quantity of hydrogen actually combined with a little bit less than eight times its mass of oxygen. Therefore if the atomic weight of hydrogen were considered to be 1, the atomic weight of oxygen would have to be not 16, but 15.87.

As it happens, oxygen combines with more elements (and more easily) than hydrogen. The ratio of its atomic weight to that of other elements is also more often a whole number. In working out the atomic weight of elements it was therefore more convenient to set the atomic weight of oxygen at a whole number than that of hydrogen. Berzelius did this, for instance, in the table of atomic weights he published in 1828. At first he called the atomic weight of oxygen 100. Then he decided to

John Dalton

make the atomic weights as small as possible, without allowing any atomic weight to be less than 1. For that reason, he set the atomic weight of oxygen at exactly 16, and in that case, the atomic weight of hydrogen had to be placed just a trifle higher than 1. The atomic weight of hydrogen became 1.008. This system was retained for nearly a century and a half.

Throughout the 19th century, chemists kept on working out atomic weights more and more carefully. By the start of the 20th century, most elements had their atomic weights worked out to two decimal places, sometimes three.

A number of elements had atomic weights that were nearly whole numbers on the *oxygen = 16* standard. The atomic weight of aluminum was just about 27, that of calcium almost 40, that of carbon almost 12, that of gold almost 197, and so on.

On the other hand, some elements had atomic weights that were far removed from whole numbers. The atomic weight of chlorine was close to 35.5, that of copper to 63.5, that of iron to 55.8, that of silver to 107.9, and so on.

Throughout the 19th century, chemists did not know why so many atomic weights were whole numbers, while others weren't. They simply made their measurements and recorded what they found. For an explanation, they had to wait for a line of investigation into electricity to come to fruition.

Notes:

*"Mass" is the correct term, but "weight", which is a somewhat different thing, is so commonly used instead that in this book I won't make any distinction.

2

ELECTRICITY

Units of Electricity

Through the 18th century, scientists had been fascinated by the properties of electricity. Electricity seemed, at the time, to be a very fine fluid that could extend through ordinary matter without taking up any room.

Electricity did more than radiate through matter however. It also produced important changes in matter. In the first years of the 19th century, it was found that a current of electricity could cause different atoms or different groups of atoms to move in opposite directions through a liquid in which they were dissolved.

The English scientist Michael Faraday noted in 1832 that a given quantity of electricity seemed to liberate the same number of atoms of a variety of different elements. In some cases, though, it liberated just half the expected number of atoms or even, in a few cases, just a third.

Scientists began to speculate that electricity, like matter, might consist of tiny units. When electricity broke up a molecule, perhaps a unit of electricity attached itself to each atom. In that case, the same quantity of electricity, containing the same number of units, would liberate the same number of atoms.

In the case of some elements, each atom could attach 2 units of electricity to itself, or perhaps even 3. When that happened a given quantity of electricity would liberate only one-half, or only one-third, the usual number of atoms. (Thus, 18 units of electricity would liberate 18 atoms if distributed 1 to an atom; only 9 atoms if distributed 2 to an atom; and only 6 atoms if distributed 3 to an atom.)

Michael Faraday's Laboratory at the Royal Institute

It was understood at the time that electricity existed in two varieties—*positive* and *negative*. It appeared that if an atom attached a positive unit of electricity to itself it would be pulled in one direction through the solution by the voltage. If it attached a negative unit of electricity to itself it would be pulled in the other direction.

The units of electricity were a great deal more difficult to study than the atomic units of matter, and throughout the 19th century they remained elusive. But, in 1891, the Irish physicist George Johnstone Stoney suggested that the supposed unit of electricity be given a name at least. He called the unit an *electron*.

Cathode Rays

An electric current flows through a closed circuit of some conducting material, such as metal wires. It starts at one pole of a battery, or of some other electricity generating device, and ends at the other. The two poles are the positive pole or *anode* and the negative pole or *cathode*.

If there is a break in the circuit, the current will usually not flow at all. If, however, the break is not a large one, and the current is under a high driving force, or *voltage,* then the current may leap across the break. If two ends of a wire, making up part of a broken circuit, are brought close to each other with nothing but air between, a spark may leap across the narrowing gap before they actually meet and, while it persists, the current will flow despite the break.

The light of the spark, and the crackling sound it makes, are the results of the electric current interacting with molecules of air and heating them. Neither the light nor the sound is the electricity itself. In order to detect the electricity, the current ought to be forced across a gap containing nothing, not even air.

In order to do that, wires would have to be sealed into a glass tube from which all (or almost all) the air was withdrawn. This was not easy to do and it was not until 1854 that Heinrich Geissler, a German glassblower and inventor, accomplished this feat. The wires sealed into such a *Geissler tube* could be attached to the poles of an electric generator, and if enough voltage was built up, the current would leap across the vacuum.

Such experiments were first performed by the German physicist Julius Plücker. In 1858 he noticed that when the current flowed across the vacuum there was a greenish glow about the wire that was attached to the cathode of the generator. Others studied this glow and finally the German physicist Eugen Goldstein decided in 1876 that there were rays of some sort beginning at the wire attached to the negatively charged cathode and ending at the part of the tube opposite the cathode. He called them *cathode rays*.

These cathode rays, it seemed, might well be the electric current itself, freed from the metal wires that usually carried it. If so, determining the nature of the cathode rays might reveal a great deal about the nature of the electric current. Were cathode rays something like light and were they made up of tiny waves? Or were they a stream of particles possessing mass?

There were physicists on each side of the question. By 1885, however, the English physicist William Crookes showed that cathode rays could be made to turn a small wheel when they struck that wheel on one side. This seemed to show that the cathode rays possessed mass and were a stream of atom-like particles, rather than a beam of mass-less light. Furthermore, Crookes showed that the cathode rays could be pushed sideways in the presence of a magnet. (This effect, when current flows in a wire, is what makes a motor work.) This meant that, unlike either light or ordinary atoms, the cathode rays carried an electric charge.

This view of the cathode rays as consisting of a stream of electrically charged particles was confirmed by another English physicist, Joseph John Thomson. In 1897 he showed that the cathode rays could also be made to take a curved path in the presence of electrically charged objects. The particles making up the cathode rays were charged with negative electricity, judging from the direction in which they were made to curve by electrically charged objects.

Thomson had no hesitation in maintaining that these particles carried the units of electricity that Faraday's work had

Wilhelm Roentgen

hinted at. Eventually, Stoney's name for the units of electricity was applied to the particles that carried those units. The cathode rays, in other words, were considered to be made up of streams of electrons and Thomson is usually given credit for having discovered the electron.

The extent to which cathode rays curved in the presence of a magnet or electrically charged objects depended on the size of the electric charge on the electrons and on the mass of the electrons. Ordinary atoms could be made to carry an electric charge and by comparing their behavior with those of electrons, some of the properties of electrons could be determined.

There were, for instance, good reasons to suppose that the electron carried a charge of the same size as one that a hydrogen atom could be made to carry. The electrons, however, were much easier to pull out of their straight-line path than the charged hydrogen atom was. The conclusion drawn from this was that the electron had much less mass than the hydrogen atom.

Thomson was able to show, indeed, that the electron was much lighter than the hydrogen atom, which was the lightest of all the atoms. Nowadays we know the relationship quite exactly. We know that it would take 1837.11 electrons to possess the mass of a single hydrogen atom. The electron is therefore a *subatomic particle,* the first of this sort to be discovered.

In 1897, then, two types of mass-containing particles were known. There were the atoms, which made up ordinary matter, and the electrons, which made up electric current.

Radioactivity

Was there a connection between these two sets of particles—atoms and electrons? In 1897, when the electron was discovered, a line of research that was to tie the two kinds of particles together had already begun.

In 1895 the German physicist Wilhelm Konrad Roentgen was working with cathode rays. He found that if he made the cathode rays strike the glass at the other end of the tube, a kind of radiation was produced. This radiation was capable of penetrating glass and other matter. Roentgen had no idea as to the nature of the radiation, and so called it *X rays*. This name, containing *X* for *unknown,* was retained even after physicists worked out the nature of X rays and found them to be light-like radiation made up of waves much shorter than those of ordinary light.

At once, physicists became fascinated with X rays and began searching for them everywhere. One of those involved in the search was the French physicist Antoine Henri Becquerel. A certain compound, potassium uranyl sulfate, glowed after being exposed to sunlight and Becquerel wondered if this glow, like the glow on the glass in Roentgen's X-ray tube, contained X rays.

It did, but while investigating the problem in 1896, Becquerel found that the compound was giving off invisible penetrating X-ray-like radiation continually, whether it was exposed to sunlight or not. The radiation was detected because it would fog a photographic plate just as light would. What's more, the radiation would fog the plate, even if the plate were wrapped in black paper, so that it could penetrate matter just as X rays could.

Others, in addition to Becquerel, were soon investigating the new phenomenon. In 1898 the Polish (later French) physicist Marie Sklodowska Curie showed that it was the uranium atom that was the source of the radiation, and that any compound containing the uranium atom would give off these penetrating rays.

Until then, uranium had not been of much interest to chemists. It was a comparatively rare metal that was first discovered in 1789 by the German chemist Martin Heinrich Klaproth. It had no particular uses and remained an obscure element. As chemists learned to work out the atomic weights of the various elements, they found, however, that, of the elements then known, uranium had the highest atomic weight of all—238.

Once uranium was discovered to be an endless source of radiation, it gained interest that has risen ever since. Madame Curie gave the name *radioactivity* to this phenomenon of continuously giving off rays. Uranium was the first element found to be radioactive.

Marie Curie

It did not remain alone however. It was soon shown that thorium was also radioactive. Thorium, which had been discovered in 1829 by Berzelius, was made up of atoms that were the second most massive known at the time. Thorium's atomic weight is 232.

But what was the mysterious radiation emitted by uranium and thorium?

Almost at once it was learned that whatever the radiation was, it was not uniform in properties. In 1899 Becquerel (and others) showed that, in the presence of a magnet, some of the radiation swerved in a particular direction. Later it was found that a portion of it swerved in the opposite direction. Still another part didn't swerve at all but moved on in a straight line.

The conclusion was that uranium and thorium gave off three kinds of radiation. One carried a positive charge of electricity, one a negative charge, and one no charge at all. The New Zealand-born physicist Ernest Rutherford called the first two kinds of radiation *alpha rays* and *beta rays,* after the first two letters of the Greek alphabet. The third was soon called *gamma rays* after the third letter.

The gamma rays eventually turned out to be another light-like form of radiation, with waves even shorter than those of X rays. The alpha rays and beta rays, which carried electric charges, seemed to be streams of charged particles (*alpha particles* and *beta particles*) just as the cathode rays had turned out to be.

In 1900, indeed, Becquerel studied the beta particles and found them to be identical in mass and charge with electrons. They *were* electrons.

By 1906 Rutherford had worked out the nature of the alpha particles. They carried a positive electric charge that was twice as great as the electron's negative charge. If an electron carried a charge that could be symbolized as $-$, then the charge of the alpha particle was $++$. Furthermore, the alpha particle was much more massive than the electron. It was, indeed, as massive as a helium atom (the second lightest known atom) and four times as massive as a hydrogen atom. Nevertheless, the alpha particle can penetrate matter in a way in which atoms cannot, so that it seems much smaller in diameter than atoms are. The alpha particle, despite its mass, is another subatomic particle.

Here, then, is the meeting point of electrons and of atoms—the particles of electricity and of matter.

Ever since Dalton had first advanced the atomic theory over a century earlier, chemists had assumed that atoms were the fundamental units of matter. They had assumed atoms were as small as anything could be and that they could not possibly be broken up into anything smaller. The discovery of the electron, however, had shown that some particles, at least, might be far smaller than any atom. Then, the investigations into radioactivity had shown that atoms of uranium and thorium spontaneously broke up into smaller particles, including electrons and alpha particles.

It would seem, then, that atoms of these elements and presumably of all elements were made up of still smaller particles, and that among these particles were electrons. The atom had a structure, and physicists became interested in discovering exactly what that structure was.

The Structure of the Atom

Since radioactive atoms gave off either positively charged particles or negatively charged particles, it seemed reasonable to assume that atoms generally were made up of both types of electricity. Furthermore, since the atoms in matter generally carried no charge at all, the normal *neutral atom* must be made up of equal quantities of positive charge and negative charge.

It turned out that only radioactive atoms, such as those of uranium and thorium, gave off positively charged alpha particles. Many atoms, however, that were not radioactive could be made to give off electrons. In 1899 Thomson showed that certain perfectly normal metals with no trace of radioactivity gave off electrons when exposed to ultraviolet light. (This is called the *photoelectric effect*.)

It was possible to suppose, then, that the main structure of the atom was positively charged and generally immovable, and that there were also present light electrons, which could easily be detached. Thomson had suggested, as early as 1898, that the atom was a ball of matter carrying a positive charge and that individual electrons were stuck throughout its substance, like raisins in pound cake.

If something like the Thomson view were correct then the number of electrons, each with one unit of negative electricity, would depend on the total size of the positive charge carried by the atom. If the charge were +5, there would have to be 5 electrons present to balance that. The total charge would then be 0 and the atom as a whole would be electrically neutral.

If, in such a case, an electron were removed, the atomic charge of +5 would be balanced by only 4 electrons with a total charge of −4. In that case, the net charge of the atom as a whole would be +1. On the other hand, if an extra electron were forced onto the atom, the charge of +5 would be balanced by 6 electrons with a total charge of −6, and the net charge of the atom as a whole would be −1.

Such electrically charged atoms were called *ions* and their existence had been suspected since Faraday's day. Faraday had known that atoms had to travel through a solution under the influence of an electric field to account for the way in which metals and gases appeared at the cathode and anode. It was he who first used the term, ion, from a Greek word meaning *traveller*. The word had been suggested to him by the English scholar, William Whewell. In 1884 the Swedish chemist Svante August Arrhenius had first worked out a detailed theory based on the suggestion that these ions were atoms or groups of atoms that carried an electric charge.

By the close of the 19th century, then, Arrhenius's suggestion seemed correct. There were positive ions made up of atoms or groups of atoms, from which one or more of the electrons within the atoms had been removed. There were negative ions made up of single atoms or of groups of atoms, to which one or more extra electrons had been added.

Although Thomson's model of the atom explained the existence of ions and the fact that atoms could give off electrons or absorb them, it was not satisfactory in all ways. Further investigations yielded results not compatible with the raisins-in-the-pound-cake notion.

In 1906 Rutherford began to study what happened when massive subatomic particles, such as alpha particles, passed

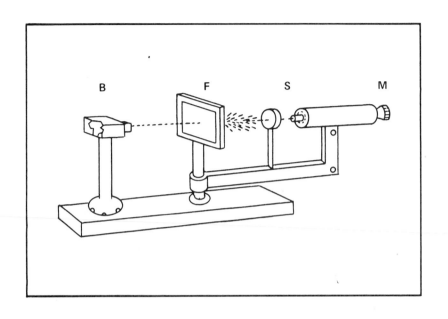

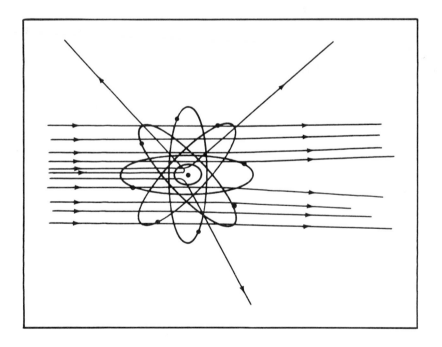

through matter. When alpha particles passed through a thin film of gold, for instance, they raced through, for the most part, as though nothing were there. The alpha particles seemed to push the light electrons aside and to act as though the positively charged main body of the atom that Thomson had pictured was not solid, but was soft and spongy.

The only trouble was that every once in a while an alpha particle seemed to strike something in the gold film and bounce to one side. Sometimes it even bounced directly backward. It was as though somewhere in each atom there was something at least as massive as the alpha particle.

How large was this massive portion of the atom? It couldn't be very large for if it were the alpha particles would hit it frequently. Instead, the alpha particles made very few hits. This meant the massive portion was very small and that most alpha particles tore through the atom without coming anywhere near it.

By 1911 Rutherford announced his results to the world. He suggested that just about all the mass of the atom was concentrated into a very tiny, positively charged *nucleus* at its center. The diameter of the nucleus was only about 1/10,000 the diameter of the atom. All the rest of the atom was filled with the very light electrons.

According to Rutherford's notion, the atom consisted of a single tiny positively charged lead shot at the center of a foam of electrons. It was Thomson's notion in reverse. Still, the nucleus carried a positive charge of a particular size and was balanced by negatively charged electrons. Rutherford's model of the atom explained the existence of ions just as easily as Thomson's did and it explained more besides.

Rutherford's alpha particle bombardment apparatus. A piece of radium in the lead box (B) emits alpha particles that go through the gold foil (F). These particles are scattered at different angles onto the fluorescent screen (S), where the flashes caused by each impact are seen through the microscope (M). Below, alpha particles are shown bouncing off a nucleus in the gold foil.

27

For instance, if all the electrons are removed so that only the nucleus remains, this nucleus is as massive as an atom but is so tiny in size that it can penetrate matter. The alpha particle would be a bare atomic nucleus from this point of view.

Rutherford's model of the *nuclear atom* is still accepted today.

Atomic Numbers

Since the atom consisted of a positively charged nucleus at the center, and a number of negatively charged electrons outside, the next step was to find the exact size of the nuclear charge and the exact number of electrons for the different varieties of atoms.

The answer came through a line of research that began with the English physicist Charles Glover Barkla. In 1911 he noted that when X rays passed through atoms, some were absorbed and some bounced back. Those that bounced back had a certain ability to penetrate other matter. When the X rays struck atoms of high atomic weight, the X rays that bounced back were particularly penetrating. In fact, each different type of atom seemed associated with reflected X rays of a particular penetrating power, so Barkla called these *characteristic X rays.*

In 1913 another English physicist, Henry Gwyn-Jeffreys Moseley, went into the matter more thoroughly. He measured the exact wavelength of the characteristic X rays by reflecting them from certain crystals. In crystals, atoms are arranged in regular order and at known distances from each other. X rays reflecting from (or more accurately, diffracting from) crystals are bent out of their path by the rows of atoms. The longer their waves, the more they are bent. From the degree of bending the wavelength of the waves can be determined.

Moseley found that the greater the atomic weight of an atom, the shorter the waves of the characteristic X rays associated with it and the more penetrating those X rays were. There was such a close connection, in fact, that Moseley could arrange the elements in order according to the wavelength of the characteristic X rays.

For some 40 years prior to this, the elements had been listed in order of atomic weight. This was useful especially since the Russian chemist Dmitri I. Mendeléev had arranged them in a *periodic table* based on the atomic weight order in such a way that elements of similar properties were grouped together. The elements in this table were sometimes numbered consecutively (*atomic number*) but this was inconvenient since, when new elements were discovered, the list of atomic numbers might have to be reorganized.

The Danish physicist Niels Bohr had just advanced a theory of atomic structure that made it reasonable to suppose that the wavelength of the characteristic X rays depended on the size of the nuclear charge of the atoms making up a particular element. Moseley therefore suggested that these X rays be used to determine the size of the positive charge on its nucleus. The atomic number could then be set equal to that charge and be made independent of new discoveries of elements.

Hydrogen, for instance, has an atomic number of 1. Its nucleus carries a unit positive charge, $+1$, and the hydrogen atom possesses 1 electron to balance this. Helium, with an atomic number of 2, has a nuclear charge of $+2$ and 2 electrons, with a total charge of -2, to balance it. (The alpha particle released by radioactive atoms is identical with a helium nucleus.)

The atomic number increases as one goes up the line of atoms. Oxygen atoms, for instance, have an atomic number of 8 and iron atoms have one of 26. At the upper end, thorium is 90 and uranium is 92. Each uranium atom has a nucleus bearing a charge of $+92$ and contains 92 electrons to balance this. Once the notion of the atomic number was worked out, it became possible to tell for certain whether any elements remained as yet undiscovered and, if so, where in the list they might be.

Thus, when Moseley first presented scientists with the atomic number it turned out that there were still 7 elements that were not discovered. At least elements with atomic numbers of 43, 61, 72, 75, 85, 87, and 91 were still not known. By 1945, all seven had been discovered. It quickly turned out that the atomic number was more fundamental and more characteristic of a particular element than was the atomic weight.

Lord Rutherford and J. A. Ratcliffe at the Cavendish Laboratory. "Talk Softly Please" was a reminder to all that this newly developed system of counting alpha particles automatically was sensitive to speech.

Since Dalton's time it had been assumed that all the atoms of a particular element were of equal atomic weight and that atoms of two different elements were always of different atomic weight. The first inkling and the first proof that this might not be so came through the study of radioactivity.

Isotopes

In 1902 Rutherford and his co-worker Frederick Soddy showed that when uranium atoms gave off alpha particles, a new kind of atom was formed that was not uranium at all. It was this new atom that was eventually found to give off a beta particle, and then another atom of still another element was formed. This work of Rutherford and Soddy began a line of investigation that by 1907 had shown that there was a whole radioactive chain of elements, each one breaking down to the next in line by giving off either an alpha particle or a beta particle, until finally a lead atom was formed that was not radioactive.

There was, in short, a *radioactive series* beginning with uranium (atomic number 92) and ending with lead (atomic number 82). The same was true of thorium (atomic number 90), which began a series that also ended with lead. Still a third element, actinium (atomic number 89) was, at that time, the first known member of a series that also ended in lead.

The various atoms formed in these three radioactive series were not all different in every way. When the uranium atom gives off an alpha particle, it forms an atom originally called *uranium X_1*. On close investigation, it turned out that this uranium X_1 had the chemical properties of thorium. Uranium X_1 had, however, radioactive properties different from ordinary thorium.

Uranium X_1 broke down so rapidly, giving off beta particles as it did so, that half of any given quantity would have broken down in 24 days. Another way of saying this (which was introduced by Rutherford) was that the *half-life* of uranium X_1 is 24 days. Ordinary thorium, however, gives off alpha particles, not beta particles, and does so at such a slow rate that its half-life is 14 billion years!

Uranium X_1 and ordinary thorium were in the same place in the list of elements by chemical standards, and yet there was clearly something different about the two.

Here is another case. In 1913 the British chemist Alexander Fleck studied *radium B* and *radium D,* the names given to two different kinds of atoms in the uranium radioactive series. He also studied *thorium B* in the thorium radioactive series and *actinium B* in the actinium radioactive series. All four are chemically the same as ordinary lead; all four are in the same place in the list of elements. Yet each is different from the radioactive standpoint. Though all give off beta particles, radium B has a half-life of 27 minutes, radium D one of 19 years, thorium B one of 11 hours, and actinium B one of 36 minutes.

In 1913 Soddy called atoms that were in the same place in the list of elements, but which had different radioactive properties, *isotopes,* from Greek words meaning *same place.*

At first, it seemed that the only difference between isotopes might be in their radioactive properties and that only radioactive atoms were involved. Quickly that proved not to be so.

It proved that it was possible to have several forms of the same element that were all different even though none of them were radioactive. The uranium series, the thorium series, and the actinium series all ended in lead. In each case the lead formed was stable (not radioactive). Were the lead atoms identical in every case? Soddy had worked out the way in which atomic weights altered every time an alpha particle or a beta particle was given off by an atom. Working through the three radioactive series he decided that the lead atoms had different atomic weights in each case.

The uranium series ought to end with lead atoms that had an atomic weight of 206. The thorium series ought to end in lead atoms with an atomic weight of 208 and the actinium series in lead atoms with an atomic weight of 207.

If this were so, there would be 3 lead isotopes that would differ not in radioactive properties, but in atomic weight. The isotopes could be referred to as lead-206, lead-207, and lead-208. If we use the chemical symbol for lead (Pb), we could write the isotopes, ^{206}Pb, ^{207}Pb, and ^{208}Pb. (We read the symbol

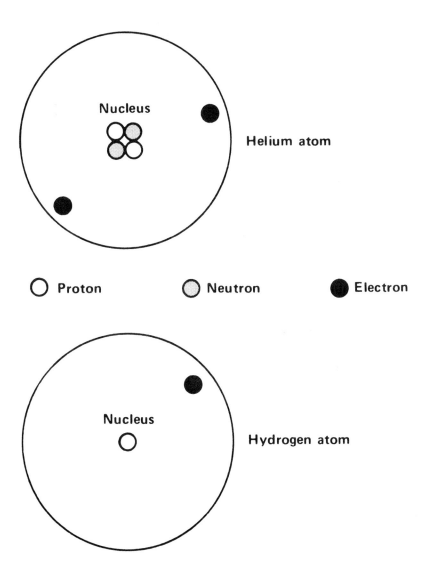

Nucleus

Helium atom

○ Proton   ◯ Neutron   ● Electron

Nucleus

Hydrogen atom

^{206}Pb as lead-206.) Atomic weight measurements made in 1914 by Soddy and others supported that theory.

All 3 lead isotopes had the same atomic number of 82. The atoms of all 3 isotopes had nuclei with an electric charge of +82 and all 3 had 82 electrons in the atom to balance that positive nuclear charge. The difference was in the mass of the nucleus only.

But what of ordinary lead that existed in the rocks far removed from any radioactive substances and that had presumably been stable through all the history of earth? Its atomic weight was 207.2.

Was the stable lead that had no connection with radioactivity made up of atoms of still another isotope, one with a fractional atomic weight? Or could stable lead be made up of a mixture of isotopes, each of a different whole-number atomic weight and was the overall atomic weight a fraction only because it was an average?

It was at the moment difficult to tell in the case of lead, but an answer came in connection with another element, the rare gas neon (atomic symbol Ne), which has an atomic weight of 20.2.

Was that fractional atomic weight something that was possessed by all neon atoms without exception or was it the average of some lightweight atoms and some heavyweight ones? It would be a matter of crucial importance if isotopes of neon could be found, for neon had nothing to do with any of the radioactive series. If neon had isotopes then any element might have them.

In 1912 Thomson was working on neon. He sent a stream of cathode-ray electrons through neon gas. The electrons smashed into the neon atoms and knocked an electron off some of them. That left a neon ion carrying a single positive charge—an ion that could be written Ne^+.

The neon ions move in the electric field as electrons do, but in the opposite direction since they have an opposite charge. In the combined presence of a magnet and of an electric field, the neon ions move in a curved path. If all the neon ions had the same mass, all would follow the same curve. If some were more massive than others, the more massive ones would curve less.

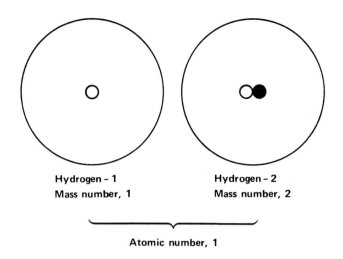

Hydrogen – 1
Mass number, 1

Hydrogen – 2
Mass number, 2

Atomic number, 1

● Neutron   ○ Proton   ☐ Electron

Helium-3
Mass number, 3

Helium – 4
Mass number, 4

Atomic number, 2

Isotopes of two elements

The neon ions ended on a photographic plate, which was darkened at the point of landing. There were two regions of darkening, because there were neon ions of two different masses that curved in two different degrees and ended in two different places. Thomson showed, from the amount of curving, that there was a neon isotope with an atomic weight of 20 and one with an atomic weight of 22—^{20}Ne and ^{22}Ne.

What's more, from the intensity of darkening, it could be seen that ordinary neon was made up of atoms that were roughly 90% ^{20}Ne and 10% ^{22}Ne. The overall atomic weight of neon, 20.2, was the average atomic weight of these 2 isotopes.

Thomson's instrument was the first one capable of separating isotopes and such instruments came to be called *mass spectrometers*. The first to use the name was the English physicist Francis William Aston, who built the first efficient instrument of this type in 1919.

He used it to study as many elements as he could. He and those who followed him located many isotopes and determined the frequency of their occurrence with considerable precision. It turned out, for instance, that neon is actually 90.9% ^{20}Ne, and 8.8% ^{22}Ne. Very small quantities of still a third isotope, ^{21}Ne, are also present, making up 0.3%.

As for ordinary lead in nonradioactive rocks, it is made up of 23.6% ^{206}Pb, 22.6% ^{207}Pb, and 52.3% ^{208}Pb. There is still a fourth isotope, ^{204}Pb, which makes up the remaining 1.5% and which is not the product of any radioactive series at all.

The isotopes always have atomic weights that are close to, but not quite, whole numbers. Any atomic weight of an element that departs appreciably from an integer does so only because it is an average of different isotopes. For instance, the atomic weight of chlorine (chemical symbol Cl) is 35.5, but this is because it is made up of a mixture of 2 isotopes. About one quarter of chlorine's atoms are ^{37}Cl and about three-quarters are ^{35}Cl.

To avoid confusion, the average mass of the isotopes that make up a particular element is still called the atomic weight of that element. The integer closest to the mass of the individual isotope is spoken of as the *mass number* of that isotope. Thus, chlorine is made up of isotopes with mass numbers 35 and 37, but the atomic weight of chlorine as it is found in nature is 35.5 (or, to be more accurate, 35.453).

In the same way, ordinary lead is made up of isotopes with mass numbers 204, 206, 207, and 208, and its atomic weight is 207.19; neon is made up of isotopes with mass numbers 20, 21, and 22, and its atomic weight is 20.183, and so on.

If the atomic weight of some element happens to be very close to a whole number to begin with, it may consist of a single kind of atom. For instance, the gas fluorine (chemical symbol F) has an atomic weight of nearly 19, while that of the metal sodium (chemical symbol Na) is nearly 23. As it turns out, all the atoms of fluorine are of the single variety ^{19}F, while all the atoms of sodium are ^{23}Na.

Sometimes the atomic weight of an element, as it occurs in nature, is nearly a whole number and yet it is made up of more than 1 isotope. In that case, one of the isotopes makes up very nearly all of it, while the others are present in such minor quantities that the average is hardly affected.

Helium, for instance (atomic symbol He) has an atomic weight of just about 4, and, indeed, almost all the atoms making it up are ^{4}He. However, 0.0001% of the atoms, or one out of a million, are ^{3}He. Again, 99.6% of all the nitrogen atoms (atomic symbol N) are ^{14}N, but 0.4% are ^{15}N. Then, 98.9% of all carbon atoms (atomic symbol C) are ^{12}C, but 1.1% are ^{13}C. It is not surprising that the atomic weights of nitrogen and carbon are just about 14 and 12, respectively.

Even hydrogen does not escape. Its atomic weight is just about 1 and most of its atoms are ^{1}H. The American chemist Harold Clayton Urey detected the existence of a more massive isotope, ^{2}H. This isotope has almost twice the mass of the lighter one. No other isotopes of a particular atom differ in mass by so large a factor. For that reason ^{2}H and ^{1}H differ in ordinary chemical properties more than isotopes usually do and Urey therefore gave ^{2}H the special name of *deuterium* from a Greek word meaning *second*.

In 1929 the American chemist William Francis Giauque found that oxygen was composed of more than 1 isotope. Its atomic weight had been set arbitrarily at 16.0000 so it was a relief that 99.76% of its atoms were ^{16}O. However, 0.20% were ^{18}O, and 0.04% were ^{17}O.

As you see, ^{16}O must have a mass number of slightly less than 16.0000 and it must be the more massive isotopes ^{17}O and ^{18}O that pull the average up to 16.0000. Disregarding this, chemists clung to a standard atomic weight of 16.000 for oxygen as it appeared in nature, preferring not to concern themselves with the separate isotopes.

Physicists, however, felt uneasy at using an average as standard for they were more interested in working with individual isotopes. They preferred to set ^{16}O at 16.0000 so that the average atomic weight of oxygen was 16.0044 and all other atomic weights rose in proportion. Atomic weights determined by this system were *physical atomic weights*.

Finally, in 1961, a compromise was struck. Chemists and physicists alike decided to consider the atomic weight of ^{12}C as exactly 12 and to use that as a standard. By this system, the atomic weight of oxygen became 15.9994, which is only very slightly less than 16.

The radioactive elements did not escape this new view either. The atomic weight of uranium (chemical symbol U) is just about 238 and, indeed, most of its atoms are ^{238}U. In 1935, however, the Canadian-American physicist, Arthur Jeffrey Dempster, found that 0.7% of its atoms were a lighter isotope, ^{235}U.

These differed considerably in radioactive properties. The common uranium isotope, ^{238}U, had a half-life of 4500 million years, while ^{235}U had a half-life of only 700 million years. Furthermore ^{235}U broke down in three stages to actinium. It was ^{235}U, not actinium itself, that was the beginning of the actinium radioactive series.

As for thorium (atomic symbol Th) with an atomic weight of 232, it did indeed turn out that in the naturally occurring element virtually all the atoms were ^{232}Th.

3

ENERGY

The Law of Conservation of Energy

We have now gone as far as we conveniently can in considering the intertwining strands of the atom and of electricity. It is time to turn to the third strand—energy.

To physicists the concept of *work* is that of exerting a force on a body and making it move through some distance. To lift a weight against the pull of gravity is work. To drive a nail into wood against the friction of its fibers is work.

Anything capable of performing work is said to possess *energy* from Greek words meaning *work within*. There are various forms of energy. Any moving mass possesses energy by virtue of its motion. That is, a moving hammer will drive a nail into wood, while the same hammer held motionlessly against the nailhead will not do so. Heat is a form of energy, since it will expand steam that will force wheels into motion that can then do work. Electricity, magnetism, sound, and light can be made to perform work and are forms of energy.

The forms of energy are so many and so various that scientists were eager to find some rule that covered them all and would therefore serve as a unifying bond. It did not seem impossible that such a rule might exist, since one had been found in connection with matter that appeared in even greater variety than energy did.

All matter, whatever its form and shape, possessed mass, and in the 1770's, the French chemist Antoine Laurent Lavoisier discovered that the quantity of mass was constant. If a system of matter were isolated and made to undergo complicated chemical reactions, everything about it might change, but not its mass. A solid might turn into a gas; a single substance might change into two or three different substances, but whatever happened, the total mass at the end was exactly the same (as nearly as chemists could tell) as at the beginning. None was either created or destroyed; however, the nature of the matter might change. This was called the *law of conservation of mass.*

Naturally, it would occur to scientists to wonder if a similar law might hold for energy. The answer wasn't easy to get. It wasn't as simple to measure the quantity of energy as it was to measure the quantity of mass. Nor was it as simple to pen up a quantity of energy and keep it from escaping or from gaining additional quantity from outside, as it was in the case of mass.

Beginning in 1840, however, the English physicist James Prescott Joule began a series of experiments in which he made use of every form of energy he could think of. In each case he turned it into heat and allowed the heat to raise the temperature of a given quantity of water. He used the rise in temperature as a measure of the energy. By 1847 he was convinced that any form of energy could be turned into fixed and predictable amounts of heat; that a certain amount of work was equivalent to a certain amount of heat.

In that same year, the German physicist Hermann Ludwig Ferdinand von Helmholtz advanced the general notion that a fixed amount of energy in one form was equal to the same amount of energy in any other form. Energy might change its form over and over, but not change its amount. None could either be destroyed or created. This is the *law of conservation of energy.*

Chemical Energy

There is energy in a piece of wood. Left quietly to itself, it seems completely incapable of bringing about any kind of work. Set it on fire, however, and the wood plus the oxygen in the air will give off heat and light that are clearly forms of energy. The heat could help boil water and run a steam engine.

The amount of energy in burning wood could be measured if it were mixed with air and allowed to burn in a closed container that was immersed in a known quantity of water. From the rise in temperature of the water, the quantity of energy produced could be measured in units called *calories* (from a Latin word for *heat*). The instrument was therefore called a *calorimeter*.

In the 1860's the French chemist Pierre Eugène Marcelin Berthelot carried through hundreds of such determinations. His work and similar work by others made it clear that such *chemical energy*—the energy derived from chemical changes in matter—fit the law of conservation of energy.

By the end of the 19th century, energy could be explained in this way. Molecules are composed of combinations of atoms. Within the molecules, the atoms stick together more or less tightly. It takes a certain amount of energy to pull a molecule apart into separate atoms against the resistance of the forces holding them together.

If, after being pulled apart, the atoms are allowed to come together again, they give off energy. The amount of energy they give off in coming together is exactly equal to the amount of energy they had to gain before they could separate.

This is true of all substances. For instance, hydrogen gas, as it is found on earth, is made up of molecules containing 2 hydrogen atoms each (H_2). Add a certain amount of energy and you pull the atoms apart; allow the atoms to come back together into paired molecules, and the added energy is given back again. The same is true for the oxygen molecule, which is made up of 2 oxygen atoms (O_2) and of the water molecule (H_2O). Always the amount of energy absorbed in one change is given off in the opposite change. The amount absorbed and the amount given off are always exactly equal.

However, the amount of energy involved differs from molecule to molecule. It is quite hard to pull hydrogen molecules apart, and it is even harder to pull oxygen molecules apart. You have to supply about 12% more energy to pull an oxygen molecule apart than to pull a hydrogen molecule apart. Naturally, if you let 2 oxygen atoms come together to form an oxygen molecule, you get back 12% more energy than if you allow 2 hydrogen atoms to come together to form a hydrogen molecule.

It takes a considerably larger amount of energy to pull apart a water molecule into separate atoms than to pull apart either hydrogen or oxygen molecules. Naturally, that greater energy is also returned once the hydrogen and oxygen atoms are allowed to come back together into water molecules.

Next, imagine pulling apart hydrogen and oxygen molecules into hydrogen and oxygen atoms and then having those atoms come together to form *water* molecules. A certain amount of energy is put into the system to break up the hydrogen and oxygen molecules, but then a much greater amount of energy is given off when the water molecules form.

It is for that reason that a great deal of energy (mostly in the form of heat) is given off if a jet of hydrogen gas and a jet of oxygen gas are allowed to mix in such a way as to form water.

Just mixing the hydrogen and oxygen isn't enough. The molecules of hydrogen and oxygen must be separated and that takes a little energy. The energy in a match flame is enough to raise the temperature of the mixture and to make the hydrogen and oxygen molecules move about more rapidly and more energetically. This increases the chance that some molecules will be broken up into separate atoms (though the actual process is rather complicated). An oxygen atom might then strike a hydrogen molecule to form water ($O + H_2 \rightarrow H_2O$) and more energy is given off than was absorbed from the match flame. The temperature goes up still higher so that further breakup among the oxygen and hydrogen molecules is encouraged.

This happens over and over again so that in very little time, the temperature is very high and the hydrogen and oxygen are combining to form water at an enormous rate. If a great deal of hydrogen and oxygen are well-mixed to begin with, the rate of reaction is so great that an explosion occurs.

Such a situation, in which each reacting bit of the system adds energy to the system by its reaction and brings about more reactions like itself, is called a *chain reaction*. Thus, a match flame put to one corner of a large sheet of paper will set that corner burning. The heat of the burning will ignite a neighboring portion of the sheet and so on till the entire sheet is burned. For that matter a single smoldering cigarette end can serve to burn down an entire forest in a vastly destructive chain reaction.

Electrons and Energy

At the turn of the century, the discovery of the structure of the atom sharpened the understanding of chemical energy. The German chemist Richard Abegg first suggested that atoms were held together through the transfer of electrons from one atom to another.

To see how this worked, one began by noting that electrons in an atom existed in a series of shells. The innermost shell could hold only 2 electrons, the next 8, the next 18 and so on. It turned out that some electron arrangements were more stable than others. If only the innermost shell contained electrons and it were filled with the 2 electrons that were all it could hold, then that was a stable arrangement. If an atom contained electrons in more than one shell and the outermost shell that held electrons held 8, that was a stable arrangement, too.

Thus, the helium atom has 2 electrons only, filling the innermost shell, and that is so stable an arrangement that helium undergoes no chemical reactions at all. The neon atom has 10 electrons—2 in the innermost shell, and 8 in the next—and it does not react. The argon atom has 18 electrons—2, 8, and 8—and it too is very stable.

But what if an atom did not have its electron shell so neatly filled? The sodium atom has 11 electrons—2, 8, and 1—while the fluorine atom has 9 electrons—2 and 7. If the sodium atom passed one of its electrons to a fluorine atom, both would have the stable configuration of neon—2 and 8. This, therefore, ought to have a great tendency to happen.

If it did happen, though, the sodium atom, minus 1 electron, would have a unit positive charge and would be Na^+, a positively charged ion. Fluorine with 1 electron in excess would become F^-, a negatively charged ion. The 2 ions, with opposite charges, would cling together, since opposite charges attract, and thus the molecule of sodium fluoride (NaF) would be formed.

In 1916 the American chemist Gilbert Newton Lewis carried this notion further. Atoms could cling together not only as a result of the outright transfer of 1 or more electrons, but through sharing pairs of electrons. This sharing could only take place if the atoms remained close neighbors, and it would take energy to pull them apart and break up the shared pool, just as it would take energy to pull 2 ions apart against the attraction of opposite charges.

In this way the vague notions of atoms clinging together in molecules and being forced apart gave way to a much more precise picture of electrons being transferred or shared. The electron shifts could be dealt with mathematically by a system that came to be called *quantum mechanics* and chemistry was thus made a more exact science than it had ever been before.

The Energy of the Sun

The most serious problem raised by the law of conservation of energy involved the sun. Until 1847, scientists did not question sunlight. The sun radiated vast quantities of energy but that apparently was its nature and was no more to be puzzled over than the fact that the earth rotated on its axis.

Once Helmholtz had stated that energy could neither be created nor destroyed, however, he was bound to ask where the sun's energy came from. It had, to man's best knowledge, been radiating heat and light, with no perceptible change, throughout the history of civilization and, from what biologists and geologists could deduce, for countless ages earlier. Where, then, did that energy come from?

The sun gave the appearance of being a huge globe of fire. Could it actually be that—a large heap of burning fuel, turning chemical energy into heat and light?

The sun's mass was known and its rate of energy production was known. Suppose the sun's mass were a mixture of hydrogen and oxygen and it were burning at a rate sufficient to produce the energy at the rate it was giving it off. If that were so, all the hydrogen and oxygen in its mass would be consumed in 1500 years. No chemical reaction in the sun could account for its having given us heat and light since the days of the pyramids, let alone since the days of the dinosaurs.

Was there some source of energy greater than chemical energy? What about the energy of motion? Helmholtz suggested that meteors might be falling into the sun at a steady rate. The energy of their collisions might then be converted into heat and light and this could keep the sun shining for as long as the supply of meteors held out—even millions of years.

This, however, would mean that the sun's mass would be increasing steadily, and so would the force of its gravitational pull. With the sun's gravitational field increasing steadily, the length of earth's year would be decreasing at a measurable rate—but it wasn't.

In 1854 Helmholtz came up with something better. He suggested that the sun was contracting. Its outermost layers were falling inward, and the energy of this fall was converted into heat and light. What's more, this energy would be obtained without any change in the mass of the sun whatever.

Helmholtz calculated that the sun's contraction over the 6000 years of recorded history would have reduced its diameter only 560 miles—a change that would not have been noticeable to the unaided eye. Since the development of the telescope, two and a half centuries earlier, the decrease in diameter would have been only 23 miles and that was not measurable by the best techniques of Helmholtz's day.

Working backward, however, it seemed that 25 million years ago, the sun must have been so large as to fill the earth's orbit. Clearly the earth could not then have existed. In that case, the maximum age of the earth was only 25 million years.

Geologists and biologists found themselves disturbed by this. The slow changes in the earth's crust and in the evolution of life made it seem very likely that the earth must have been in existence—with the sun delivering heat and light very much in the present fashion—for many hundreds of millions of years.

Yet there seemed absolutely no other way of accounting for the sun's energy supply. Either the law of conservation of energy was wrong (which seemed unlikely), or the painfully collected evidence of geologists and biologists was wrong (which seemed unlikely),—or there was some source of energy greater than any known in the 19th century, whose existence had somehow escaped mankind (which also seemed unlikely).

Yet one of those unlikely alternatives would have to be true. And then in 1896 came the discovery of radioactivity.

ENERGY

The Energy of Radioactivity

Scientists could see that radioactivity involved the giving off of energy. Uranium emitted gamma rays that we now know to be a hundred thousand times as energetic as ordinary light rays. What's more, alpha particles were being emitted at velocities of perhaps 30,000 kilometers per second, while the lighter beta particles were being shot off at velocities of up to 250,000 kilometers per second (about 0.8 times the velocity of light).

At first, the total energy given off by radioactive substances seemed so small that there was no use worrying about it. The amount of energy liberated by a gram of uranium in 1 second of radioactivity was an insignificant fraction of the energy released by a burning candle.

In a few years, however, something became apparent. A lump of uranium might give off very little energy in a second, but it kept on for second after second, day after day, month after month, and year after year with no perceptible decrease. The energy released by the uranium over a very long time grew to be enormous. It eventually turned out that while the rate at which uranium delivered energy did decline, it did so with such unbelievable slowness that it took 4.5 billion years (!) for that rate to decrease to half what it was to begin with.

If *all* the energy delivered by a gram of uranium in the course of its radioactivity over many billions of years was totaled, it was enormously greater than the energy produced by the burning of a candle with a mass equal to that of uranium.

Let's put it another way. We might think of a single uranium atom breaking down and shooting off an alpha particle. We might also think of a single carbon atom combining with 2 oxygen atoms to form carbon dioxide. The uranium atom would give off 2,000,000 times as much energy in breaking down, as the carbon atom would in combining.

The energy of radioactivity is millions of times as intense as the energy released by chemical reactions. The first reason mankind had remained unaware of radioactivity and very aware of chemical reactions was, that the most common radioactive

46

Marie and Pierre Curie

processes are so slow that their great energies were stretched over such enormous blocks of time as to be insignificant on a per second basis.

Secondly, chemical reactions are easily controlled by changing quantities, concentrations, temperatures, pressures, states of mixtures, and so on, and this makes them easy to take note of and to study. The rate of radioactive changes, however, could not apparently be altered. The early investigators quickly found that the breakdown of uranium-238, for instance, could not be hastened by heat, pressure, changes in chemical combination, or, indeed, anything else they could think of. It remained incredibly slow.

But, radioactivity was at last discovered, and the intensity of its energies was recognized and pointed out in 1902 by Marie Curie and her husband Pierre Curie.

Yet the Curies still could not explain where the energy came from. Did it come from the outside? Could the radioactive atoms somehow collect energy from their surroundings, concentrate it several million-fold, and then let it out all at once?

To concentrate energy in this fashion would violate something called *the second law of thermodynamics,* first proposed in 1850 by the German physicist Rudolf Julius Emmanuel Clausius. This law had proved so useful that physicists did not like to abandon it unless they absolutely had to.

An equally problematic possibility was that radioactive atoms were creating energy out of nothing. This theory violated the law of conservation of energy (also called *the first law of thermodynamics*), and physicists preferred not to do that either.

The only theory that seemed reasonable was to suppose that somewhere within the atom was a source of energy that had never made itself evident to humanity until the discovery of radioactivity. Becquerel was one of the first to suggest this.

It might have seemed at first that only radioactive elements had this supply of energy somewhere within the atom, but in 1903 Rutherford suggested that all atoms had a vast energy supply hidden within themselves. The supply in uranium and thorium leaked slightly, so to speak, and that was all that made them different.

But if a vast supply of energy existed in atoms, it was possible that the solution to the puzzle of the sun's energy might rest there. As early as 1899 the American geologist Thomas Chrowder Chamberlin was already speculating about a possible connection between radioactivity and the sun's energy.

If it were some variety of this newly discovered source of energy (not necessarily ordinary radioactivity, of course) that powered the sun—millions of times as intense as chemical energy—then the sun might be pouring out energy for hundreds of millions of years without perceptible physical change—just as uranium would show scarcely any change even in so mighty a time span. The sun would not have to be contracting; it would not have had to fill the earth's orbit 25,000,000 years ago.

What is involved then in radioactivity and in the sun is *nuclear energy*. That is the proper name for it. In the next chapters we will consider the subsequent history of the nuclear energy that broke upon the startled consciousness of scientists as the 20th century opened and which, less than half a century later, was to face mankind with untold consequences for good and for evil.

PERIODIC TABLE OF THE ELEMENTS

I			
H			

I	II	III	IV
3 Li	4 Be	5 B	6 C
11 Na	12 Mg	13 Al	14 Si

IA	IIA	IIIB	IVB	VB	VIB	VIIB		VIII	
19 K	20 Ca	21 Sc	22 Ti	23 V	24 Cr	25 Mn	26 Fe	27 Co
37 Rb	38 Sr	39 Y	40 Zr	41 Nb	42 Mo	43 Tc	44 Ru	45 Rh
55 Cs	56 Ba	57 * La	72 Hf	73 Ta	74 W	75 Re	76 Os	77 Ir
87 Fr	88 Ra	89 ** Ac						

* Lanthanons

** Actinons

58 Ce	59 Pr	60 Nd	61 Pm
90 Th	91 Pa	92 U	93 Np

			V		VI		VII		O
			7 N		8 O		9 F		10 Ne
			15 P		16 S		17 Cl		18 Ar

	IB	IIB	IIIA	IVA	VA	VIA	VIIA	O
8 Ni	29 Cu	30 Zn	31 Ga	32 Ge	33 As	34 Se	35 Br	36 Kr
6 Pd	47 Ag	48 Cd	49 In	50 Sn	51 Sb	52 Te	53 I	54 Xe
8 Pt	79 Au	80 Hg	81 Tl	82 Pb	83 Bi	84 Po	85 At	86 Rn

2 Sm	63 Eu	64 Gd	65 Tb	66 Dy	67 Ho	68 Er	69 Tm	70 Yb	71 Lu
4 Pu	95 Am	96 Cm	97 Bk	98 Cf	99 E	100 Fm	101 Mv	102 No	103 Lw

2 He

MASS AND ENERGY

The sheer size of the energy store in the atom's nucleus—millions of times that known to exist in the form of chemical energy—seemed unbelievable at first. Yet that size quickly came to make sense as a result of a line of research that seemed, at the beginning, to have nothing to do with energy.

Suppose a ball were thrown forward at a velocity of 20 kilometers an hour by a man on top of a flatcar that is moving forward at 20 kilometers an hour. To someone watching from the roadside the ball would appear to be travelling at 40 kilometers an hour. The velocity of the thrower is added to the velocity of the ball.

If the ball were thrown forward at 20 kilometers an hour by a man on top of a flatcar that is moving backward at 20 kilometers an hour, then the ball (to someone watching from the roadside) would seem to be not moving at all after it left the hand of the thrower. It would just drop to the ground.

There seemed no reason in the 19th century to suppose that light didn't behave in the same fashion. It was known to travel at the enormous speed of just a trifle under 300,000 kilometers per second, while earth moved in its orbit about the sun at a speed of about 30 kilometers per second. Surely if a beam of light beginning at some earth-bound source shone in the direction of earth's travel, it ought to move at a speed of 300,030 kilometers per second. If it shone in the opposite direction, against earth's motion, it ought to move at a speed of 299,970 kilometers per second.

Could such a small difference in an enormous speed be detected?

The German-American physicist Albert Abraham Michelson had invented a delicate instrument, *the interferometer*, that could compare the velocities of different beams of light with great precision. In 1887 he and a co-worker, the American chemist Edward Williams Morley, tried to measure the comparative speeds of light, using beams headed in different directions. Some of this work was performed at the U.S. Naval Academy and some at the Case Institute.

The results of the Michelson-Morley experiment were unexpected. It showed no difference in the measured speed of light. No matter what the direction of the beam—whether it went in the direction of the earth's movement, or against it, or at any angle to it—the speed of light always appeared to be exactly the same.

To explain this, the German-Swiss-American scientist Albert Einstein advanced his *special theory of relativity* in 1905. According to Einstein's view, speeds could not merely be added. A ball thrown forward at 20 kilometers an hour by a man moving at 20 kilometers an hour in the same direction would not seem to be going 40 kilometers an hour to an observer at the roadside. It would seem to be going very slightly less than 40 kilometers an hour; so slightly less that the difference couldn't be measured.

However, as speeds grew higher and higher, the discrepancy in the addition grew greater and greater (according to a formula Einstein derived) until, at velocities of tens of thousands of kilometers per hour, that discrepancy could be easily measured. At the speed of light, which Einstein showed was a limiting velocity that an observer would never reach, the discrepancy became so great that the speed of the light source, however great, added or subtracted zero to or from the speed of light.

Accompanying this were all sorts of other effects. It could be shown by Einstein's reasoning that no object possessing mass could move faster than the speed of light. What's more, as an object moved faster and faster, its length in the direction of motion (as measured by a stationary observer) grew shorter and shorter, while its mass grew greater and greater. At 260,000 kilometers per second, its length in the direction of movement was only half what it was at rest, and its mass was twice what it was. As the speed of light was approached, its length would

Albert Einstein

approach zero in the direction of motion, while its mass would approach the infinite.

Could this really be so? Ordinary objects never moved so fast as to make their lengths and masses show any measurable change. What about subatomic particles, however, which moved at tens of thousands of kilometers per second? The German physicist Alfred Heinrich Bucherer reported in 1908 that speeding electrons did gain in mass just the amount predicted by Einstein's theory. The increased mass with energy has been confimed with great precision in recent years. Einstein's special theory of relativity has met many experimental tests exactly ever since and it is generally accepted by physicists today.

Einstein's theory gave rise to something else as well. Einstein deduced that mass was a form of energy. He worked out a relationship, the *mass-energy equivalence,* that is expressed as follows:

$$E = mc^2$$

where E represents energy, m is mass, and c is the speed of light.

If mass is measured in grams and the speed of light is measured in centimeters per second, then the equation will yield the energy in a unit called *ergs.* It turns out that 1 gram of mass is equal to 900,000,000,000,000,000,000 (900 billion billion) ergs of energy. The erg is a very small unit of energy, but 900 billion billion of them mount up.

The energy equivalent of 1 gram of mass (and remember that a gram, in ordinary units, is only $1/28$ of an ounce) would keep a 100-watt light bulb burning for 35,000 years.

It is this vast difference between the tiny quantity of mass and the huge amount of energy to which it is equivalent that obscured the relationship over the years. When a chemical reaction liberates energy, the mass of the materials undergoing the reaction decreases slightly—but *very* slightly.

Suppose, for instance, a gallon of gasoline is burned. The gallon of gasoline has a mass of 2800 grams and combines with about 10,000 grams of oxygen to form carbon dioxide and water, yielding 1.35 million billion ergs. That's a lot of energy

56

and it will drive an automobile for some 25 to 30 kilometers. But by Einstein's equation all that energy is equivalent to only a little over a millionth of a gram. You start with 12,800 grams of reacting materials and you end with 12,800 grams minus a millionth of a gram or so that was given off as energy.

No instrument known to the chemists of the 19th century could have detected so tiny a loss of mass in such a large total. No wonder, then, that from Lavoisier on, scientists thought that the law of conservation of mass held exactly.

Radioactive changes gave off much more energy per atom than chemical changes did, and the percentage loss in mass was correspondingly greater. The loss of mass in radioactive changes was found to match the production of energy in just the way Einstein predicted.

It was no longer quite accurate to talk about the conservation of mass after 1905 (even though mass was almost completely conserved in ordinary chemical reactions and the law could continue to be used by chemists without trouble). Instead, it is more proper to speak of the conservation of energy, and to remember that mass was one form of energy and a very concentrated form.

The mass-energy equivalence fully explained why the atom should contain so great a store of energy. Indeed, the surprise was that radioactive changes gave off as little energy as they did. When a uranium atom broke down through a series of steps to a lead atom, it produced a million times as much energy as that same atom would release if it were involved in even the most violent of chemical changes. Nevertheless, that enormous energy change in the radioactive breakdown represented only about one-half of 1% of the total energy to which the mass of the uranium atom was equivalent.

Once Rutherford worked out the nuclear theory of the atom, it became clear from the mass-energy equivalence that the source of the energy of radioactivity was likely to be in the atomic nucleus where almost all the mass of the atom was to be found.

The attention of physicists therefore turned to the nucleus.

5

THE STRUCTURE OF THE NUCLEUS

The Proton

As early as 1886 Eugen Goldstein, who was working with cathode rays, also studied rays that moved in the opposite direction. Since the cathode rays (electrons) were negatively charged, rays moving in the opposite direction would have to be positively charged. In 1907 J. J. Thomson called them *positive rays*.

Once Rutherford worked out the nuclear structure of the atom, it seemed clear that the positive rays were atomic nuclei from which a number of electrons had been knocked away. These nuclei came in different sizes.

Were the nuclei single particles—a different one for every isotope of every element? Or were they all built up out of numbers of still smaller particles of a very limited number of varieties? Might it be that the nuclei owed their positive electrical charge to the fact that they contained particles just like the electron, but ones that carried a positive charge rather than a negative one?

All attempts to discover this *positive electron* in the nuclei failed, however. The smallest nucleus found was that produced by knocking the single electron off a hydrogen atom in one way or another. This hydrogen nucleus had a single positive charge, one that was exactly equal in size to the negative charge on the electron. The hydrogen nucleus, however, was much more massive than an electron. The hydrogen nucleus with its single positive charge was approximately 1837 times as massive as the electron with its single negative charge.

Was it possible to knock the positive charge loose from the mass of the hydrogen nucleus? Nothing physicists did could manage to do that. In 1914 Rutherford decided the attempt should be given up. He suggested that the hydrogen nucleus, for all its high mass, should be considered the unit of positive electrical charge, just as the electron was the unit of negative electrical charge. He called the hydrogen nucleus a *proton* from the Greek word for *first* because it was the nucleus of the first element.

Why the proton should be so much more massive than the electron is still one of the unanswered mysteries of physics.

The Proton-Electron Theory

What about the nuclei of elements other than hydrogen?

All the other elements had nuclei more massive than that of hydrogen and the natural first guess was that these were made up of some appropriate number of protons closely packed together. The helium nucleus, which had a mass four times as great as that of hydrogen, might be made up of 4 protons; the oxygen nucleus with a mass number of 16 might be made up of 16 protons and so on.

This guess, however, ran into immediate difficulties. A helium nucleus might have a mass number of 4 but it had an electric charge of +2. If it were made up of 4 protons, it ought to have an electric charge of +4. In the same way, an oxygen nucleus made up of 16 protons ought to have a charge of +16, but in actual fact it had one of +8.

Could it be that something was cancelling part of the positive electric charge? The only thing that could do so would be a negative electric charge* and these were to be found only on electrons as far as anyone knew in 1914. It seemed reasonable, then, to suppose that a nucleus would contain about half as many electrons in addition to the protons. The electrons were so light, they wouldn't affect the mass much, and they would succeed in cancelling some of the positive charge.

Thus, according to this early theory, *now known to be incorrect*, the helium nucleus contained not only 4 protons, but 2 electrons in addition. The helium nucleus would then have a mass number of 4 and an electric charge (atomic number) of 4 − 2, or 2. This was in accordance with observation.

This *proton-electron theory* of nuclear structure accounted for isotopes very nicely. While oxygen-16 had a nucleus made up of 16 protons and 8 electrons, oxygen-17 had one of 17 protons and 9 electrons, and oxygen-18 had one of 18 protons and 10 electrons. The mass numbers were 16, 17, and 18, respectively, but the atomic number was $16 - 8$, $17 - 9$, and $18 - 10$, or 8 in each case.

Again, uranium-238 has a nucleus built up, according to this theory, of 238 protons and 146 electrons, while uranium-235 has one built up of 235 protons and 143 electrons. In these cases the atomic number is, respectively, $238 - 146$ and $235 - 143$, or 92 in each case. The nucleus of the 2 isotopes is, however, of different structure and it is not surprising therefore that the radioactive properties of the two—properties that involve the nucleus—should be different and that the half-life of uranium-238 should be six times as long as that of uranium-235.

The presence of electrons in the nucleus not only explained the existence of isotopes, but seemed justified by two further considerations.

First, it is well known that similar charges repel each other and that the repulsion is stronger the closer together the similar charges are forced. Dozens of positively charged particles squeezed into the tiny volume of an atomic nucleus couldn't possibly remain together for more than a tiny fraction of a second. Electrical repulsion would send them flying apart at once.

On the other hand, opposite charges attract, and a proton and an electron would attract each other as strongly as 2 protons (or 2 electrons) would repel each other. It was thought possible that the presence of electrons in a collection of protons might somehow limit the repulsive force and stabilize the nucleus.

Second, there are radioactive decays in which beta particles are sent flying out of the atom. From the energy involved they could come only out of the nucleus. Since beta particles are electrons and since they come from the nucleus, it seemed to follow that there must be electrons within the nucleus to begin with.

The proton-electron theory of nuclear structure also seemed to account neatly for many of the facts of radioactivity.

Why radioactivity at all, for instance? The more complex a nucleus is, the more protons must be squeezed together and the harder, it would seem, it must be to keep them together. More and more electrons seemed to be required. Finally, when the total number of protons was 84 or more, no amount of electrons seemed sufficient to stabilize the nucleus.

The manner of breakup fits the theory, too. Suppose a nucleus gives off an alpha particle. The alpha particle is a helium nucleus made up, by this theory, of 4 protons and 2 electrons. If a nucleus loses an alpha particle, its mass number should decline by 4 and its atomic number by $4 - 2$, or 2. And, indeed, when uranium-238 (atomic number 92) gives off an alpha particle, it becomes thorium-234 (atomic number 90).

Suppose a beta particle is emitted. A beta particle is an electron and if a nucleus loses an electron, its mass number is almost unchanged. (An electron is so light that in comparison with the nucleus, we can ignore its mass.) On the other hand, a unit negative charge is gone. One of the protons in the nucleus, which had previously been masked by an electron, is now unmasked. Its positive charge is added to the rest and the atomic number goes up by one. Thus, thorium-234 (atomic number 90) gives up a beta particle and becomes protactinium-234 (atomic number 91).

If a gamma ray is given off, that gamma ray has no charge and the equivalent of very little mass. That means that neither the mass number nor the atomic number of the nucleus is changed, although its energy content is altered.

Even more elaborate changes can be taken into account. In the long run, uranium-238, having gone through many changes, becomes lead-206. Those changes include the emission of 8 alpha particles and 6 beta particles. The 8 alpha particles involve a loss of 8×4, or 32 in mass number, while the 6 beta particles contribute nothing in this respect. And, indeed, the mass number of uranium-238 declines by 32 in reaching lead-206. On the other hand the 8 alpha particles involve a decrease in atomic number of 8×2, or 16, while the 6 beta particles involve an increase in atomic number of 6×1, or 6. The total change is a decrease of $16 - 6$, or 10. And indeed, uranium (atomic number 92) changes to lead (atomic number 82).

It is useful to go into such detail concerning the proton-electron theory of nuclear structure and to describe how attractive it seemed. The theory appeared solid and unshakable and, indeed, physicists used it with considerable satisfaction for 15 years. And yet, as we shall see, it was wrong; and that should point a moral. Even the best seeming of theories may be wrong in some details and require an overhaul.

Protons in Nuclei

Let us, nevertheless, go on to describe some of the progress made in the 1920's in terms of the proton-electron theory that was then accepted.

Since a nucleus is made up of a whole number of protons, its mass ought to be a whole number if the mass of a single proton is considered 1. (The presence of electrons would add some mass but in order to simplify matters, let us ignore that.)

When isotopes were first discovered this indeed seemed to be so. However, Aston and his mass spectrometer kept measuring the mass of different nuclei more and more closely during the 1920's and found that they differed very slightly from whole numbers. Yet a fixed number of protons turned out to have different masses if they were first considered separately and then as part of a nucleus.

Using modern standards, the mass of a proton is 1.007825. Twelve separate protons would have a total mass of twelve times that, or 12.0939. On the other hand, if the 12 protons are packed together into a carbon-12 nucleus, the mass is 12 so that the mass of the individual protons is 1.000000 apiece. What happens to this difference of 0.007825 between the proton in isolation and the proton as part of a carbon-12 nucleus?

According to Einstein's special theory of relativity, the missing mass would have to appear in the form of energy. If 12 hydrogen nuclei (protons) plus 6 electrons are packed together to form a carbon nucleus, a considerable quantity of energy would have to be given off.

In general, Aston found that as one went on to more and more complicated nuclei, a larger fraction of the mass would have to appear as energy (although not in a perfectly regular way) until it reached a maximum in the neighborhood of iron.

Iron-56, the most common of the iron isotopes, has a mass number of 55.9349. Each of its 56 protons, therefore, has a mass of 0.9988.

For nuclei more complicated than those of iron, the protons in the nucleus begin to grow more massive again. Uranium-238 nuclei, for instance, have a mass of 238.0506, so that each of the 238 protons they contain has a mass of 1.0002.

By 1927 Aston had made it clear that it is the middle elements in the neighborhood of iron that are most closely and economically packed. If a very massive nucleus is broken up into somewhat lighter nuclei, the proton packing would be tighter and some mass would be converted into energy. Similarly, if very light nuclei were joined together into somewhat more massive nuclei, some mass would be converted into energy.

This demonstration that energy was released in any shift away from either extreme of the list of atoms according to atomic number fits the case of radioactivity, where very massive nuclei break down to somewhat less massive ones.

Consider that uranium-238 gives up 8 alpha particles and 6 beta particles to become lead-206. The uranium-238 nucleus has a mass of 238.0506; each alpha particle has one of 4.0026 for a total of 32.0208; each beta particle has a mass of 0.00154 for a total of 0.00924; and the lead-206 nucleus has one of 205.9745.

This means that the uranium-238 nucleus (mass: 238.0506) changes into 8 alpha particles, 6 beta particles, and a lead-206 nucleus (total mass: 238.0045). The starting mass is 0.0461 greater than the final mass and it is this missing mass that has been converted into energy and is responsible for the gamma rays and for the velocity with which alpha particles and beta particles are discharged.

Nuclear Bombardment

Once scientists realized that there was energy available when one kind of nucleus was changed into another, important questions arose. Could such a change be brought about and regulated by man? And might this not be made the source of useful power of a kind and amount previously undreamed?

Chemical energy was easy to initiate and control, since that involved the shifts of electrons on the outskirts of the atoms. Raising the temperature of a system, for instance, caused atoms to move more quickly and smash against each other harder, and that in itself was sufficient to force electrons to shift and to initiate a chemical reaction that would not take place at lower temperatures.

To shift the protons within the nucleus (*nuclear reactions*) and make nuclear energy available was a much harder problem. The particles involved were much more massive than electrons and correspondingly harder to move. What's more, they were buried deep within the atom. No temperatures available to the physicists of the 1920's could force atoms to smash together hard enough to reach and shake the nucleus.

In fact, the only objects that were known to reach the nucleus were speeding subatomic particles. As early as 1906, for instance, Rutherford had used the speeding alpha particles given off by a radioactive substance to bombard matter and to show that sometimes these alpha particles were deflected by atomic nuclei. It was, in fact, by such an experiment that he first demonstrated the existence of such nuclei.

Rutherford had continued his experiments with bombardment. An alpha particle striking a nucleus would knock it free of the atom to which it belonged and send it shooting forward, like one billiard ball hitting another. The nucleus that shot ahead would strike a film of chemical that scintillated (sparkled) under the impact. In a rough way, one could tell the kind of nucleus that struck from the nature of the sparkling.

In 1919 Rutherford bombarded nitrogen gas with alpha particles and found that he obtained the kind of sparkling he

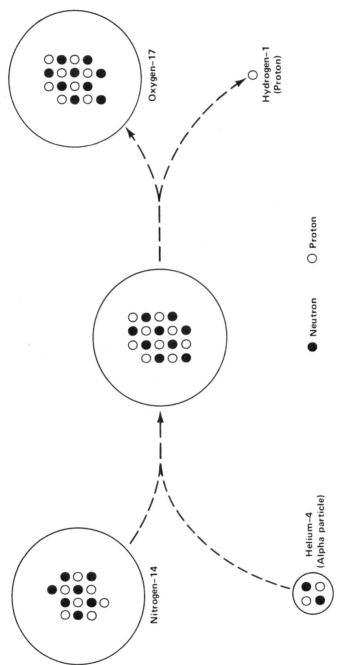

Man-made transmutation

associated with the bombardment of hydrogen gas. When he bombarded hydrogen, the alpha particles struck hydrogen nuclei (protons) and shot them forward. To get hydrogen-sparkling out of the bombardment of nitrogen, Rutherford felt, he must have knocked protons out of the nitrogen nuclei. Indeed, as was later found, he had converted nitrogen nuclei into oxygen nuclei. This was the first time in history that the atomic nucleus was altered by deliberate human act.

Rutherford continued his experiments and by 1924 had shown that alpha particles could be used to knock protons out of the nuclei of almost all elements up to potassium (atomic number 19). There were, however, limitations to the use of natural alpha particles as the bombarding agent.

First, the alpha particles used in bombardment were positively charged and so were the atomic nuclei. This meant that the alpha particles and the atomic nuclei repelled each other and much of the energy of the alpha particles was used in overcoming the repulsion. For more and more massive nuclei, the positive charge grew higher and the repulsion stronger until for elements beyond potassium, no collision could be forced, even with the most energetic naturally occurring alpha particles.

Second, the alpha particles that are sprayed toward the target cannot be aimed directly at the nuclei. An alpha particle strikes a nucleus only if, by chance, they come together. The nuclei that serve as their targets are so unimaginably small that most of the bombarding particles are sure to miss. In Rutherford's first bombardment of nitrogen, it was calculated that only 1 alpha particle out of 300,000 managed to strike a nitrogen nucleus.

The result of these considerations is clear. There is energy to be gained out of nuclear reactions, but there is also energy that must be expended to cause these nuclear reactions. In the case of nuclear bombardment by subatomic particles (the only way, apparently, in which nuclear reactions can be brought about), the energy expended seems to be many times the energy to be extracted. This is because so many subatomic particles use up their energy in ionizing atoms, knocking electrons away, and never initiate nuclear reactions at all.

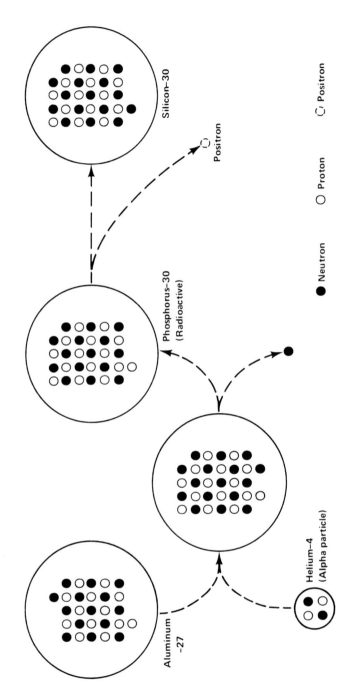

Artificial radioactivity

It was as though the only way you could light a candle would be to strike 300,000 matches, one after the other. If that were so, candles would be impractical.

In fact, the most dramatic result of alpha particle bombardment had nothing to do with energy production, but rather the reverse. New nuclei were produced that had *more* energy than the starting nuclei, so that energy was absorbed by the nuclear reaction rather than given off.

This came about first in 1934, when a French husband-and-wife team of physicists, Frédéric Joliot-Curie and Irène Joliot-Curie were bombarding aluminum-27 (atomic number 13) with alpha particles. The result was to combine part of the alpha particle with the aluminum-27 nucleus to form a new nucleus with an atomic number two units higher—15—and a mass number three units higher—30.

The element with atomic number 15 is phosphorus so that phosphorus-30 was formed. The only isotope of phosphorus that occurs in nature, however, is phosphorus-31. Phosphorus-30 was the first man-made nucleus—the first to be manufactured by nuclear reactions in the laboratory.

The reason phosphorus-30 did not occur in nature was that its energy content was too high to allow it to be stable. Its energy content drained away through the emission of particles that allowed the nucleus to change over into a stable one, silicon-30 (atomic number 14). This was an example of *artificial radioactivity*.

Since 1934, over a thousand kinds of nuclei that do not occur in nature have been formed in the laboratory through various kinds of bombardment-induced nuclear reactions. Every single one of them proved to be radioactive.

Particle Accelerators

Was there nothing that could be done to make nuclear bombardment more efficient and increase the chance of obtaining useful energy out of nuclear reactions?

In 1928 the Russian-American physicist George Gamow suggested that protons might be used as bombarding agents in

Ernest O. Lawrence holds a model of the first cyclotron in 1930, a year after its conception.

place of alpha particles. Protons were only one-fourth as massive as alpha particles and the collision might be correspondingly less effective; on the other hand, protons had only half the positive charge of alpha particles and would not be as strongly repelled by the nuclei. Then, too, protons were much more easily available than alpha particles. To get a supply of protons one only had to ionize the very common hydrogen atoms—i.e., get rid of the single electron of the hydrogen atom, and a single proton is left.

Of course, protons obtained by the ionization of hydrogen atoms have very little energy, but could energy be imparted to them? Protons carry a positive charge and a force can therefore be exerted upon them by an electric or magnetic field. In a device that makes use of such fields, protons can be accelerated (made to go faster and faster), and thus gain more and more energy. In the end, if enough energy is gained, the proton could do more damage than the alpha particle, despite the former's smaller mass. Combine that with the smaller repulsion involved and the greater ease of obtaining protons, and the weight of convenience and usefulness would swing far in the direction of the proton.

Physicists began to try to design *particle accelerators* and the first practical device of this sort was produced in 1929 by the two British physicists John Douglas Cockcroft and Ernest Thomas Sinton Walton. Their device, called an *electrostatic accelerator,* produced protons that were sufficiently energetic to initiate nuclear reactions. In 1931 they used their accelerated protons to disrupt the nucleus of lithium-7. It was the first nuclear reaction to be brought about by man-made bombarding particles.

Other types of particle accelerators were also being developed at this time. The most famous was the one built in 1930 by the American physicist Ernest Orlando Lawrence. In this device a magnet was used to make the protons move in gradually expanding circles, gaining energy with each lap until they finally moved out beyond the influence of the magnet and then hurtled out of the instrument in a straight line at maximum energy. This instrument was called a *cyclotron.*

The Cosmotron, the first accelerator to produce particles with energies greater than one billion electron volts (BeV)

The cyclotron was rapidly improved, using larger magnets and increasingly sophisticated design. There are now, at this time of writing, *proton synchrotrons* (descendants of that first cyclotron) that produce particles with over a million times the energy of those produced by Lawrence's first cyclotron. Of course, the first cyclotron was only a quarter of a meter wide, while the largest today has a diameter of some 2000 meters.

As particle accelerators grew larger, more efficient, and more powerful, they became ever more useful in studying the structure of the nucleus and the nature of the subatomic particles themselves. They did not serve, however, to bring the dream of useful nuclear energy any closer. Though they brought about the liberation of vastly more nuclear energy than Rutherford's initial bombardments could, they also consumed a great deal more energy in the process.

Rutherford, the pioneer in nuclear bombardment, was pessimistic about its potential. He maintained that it would be forever impossible to tap the energy of the nucleus for use by man. Hopes that *nuclear power* might some day run the world's industries were in his view, idle dreams.

Notes:

*The attempt to work out the structure of the nucleus resulted in a *false*, but useful, theory that persisted throughout the 1920's. The great advances in nuclear science in this decade were made in the light of this false theory and, for the sake of historical accuracy, they are so presented here. The theory now believed correct will be presented shortly, and you will see how matters can be changed from the earlier concept to the later one.

6

THE NEUTRON

Nuclear Spin

What Rutherford did not, and could not, take into account were the consequences of a completely new type of nuclear bombardment involving a type of particle unknown in the 1920's. The beginnings of the new path came about through the reluctant realization that there was a flaw in the apparently firmly grounded proton-electron picture of nuclear structure.

The flaw involved the *nuclear spin*. In 1924 the Austrian physicist Wolfgang Pauli worked out a theory that treated protons and electrons as though they were spinning on their axes. This spin could be in either direction (or, as we would say in earthly terms, from west-to-east or from east-to-west). Quantum theory has shown that a natural unit exists for what is called the angular momentum of this spin. Measured in terms of this natural unit of spin, the proton and the electron have spin ½. If the particle spun in one direction it was $+½$, if in the other it was $-½$.

When subatomic particles came together to form an atomic nucleus, each kept its original spin, and the nuclear spin was then equal to the total angular momentum of the individual particles that made it up.

For instance, suppose the helium nucleus is made up of 4 protons and 2 electrons, as was thought in the 1920's. Of the 4 protons, suppose that two had a spin of $+½$ and two of $-½$. Suppose also that of the 2 electrons, one had a spin of $+½$ and one of $-½$. All the spins would cancel each other. The total angular momentum would be zero.

Of course, it is also possible that all 6 particles were spinning in the same direction; all $+½$ or all $-½$. In that case the nuclear spin would be 3, either in one direction or the other. If 5 particles were spinning in one direction and 1 in the other, then the total spin would be 2, in one direction or the other.

In short if you have an even number of particles in a nucleus, each with a spin of $+\frac{1}{2}$ or $-\frac{1}{2}$, then the total spin is either zero or a whole number, no matter what combination of positive and negative spins you choose. (The total spin is always written as a positive number.)

On the other hand, suppose you have lithium-7, which was thought to be made up of 7 protons and 4 electrons. If the 7 protons were all $+\frac{1}{2}$ and the 4 electrons were all $-\frac{1}{2}$ in their spins, the nuclear spin would be $\frac{7}{2} - \frac{4}{2} = \frac{3}{2}$.

If you have an odd number of particles in the nucleus, you will find that any combination of positive and negative spins will *never* give you either zero or a whole number as a sum. The sum will always include a fraction.

Consequently, if one measures the spin of a particular atomic nucleus one can tell at once whether that nucleus contains an even number of particles or an odd number.

This quickly raised a problem. The nuclear spin of the common isotope, nitrogen-14, was measured accurately over and over again and turned out to be 1. There seemed no doubt about that and it could therefore be concluded that there were an even number of particles in the nitrogen-14 nucleus.

And yet, by the proton-electron theory of nuclear structure, the nitrogen-14 nucleus, with a mass number of 14 and an atomic number of 7, had to be made up of 14 protons and 7 electrons for a total of 21 particles altogether—an odd number.

The nuclear spin of nitrogen-14 indicated *even number* and the proton-electron theory indicated *odd number*. One or the other had to be wrong, but which? The nuclear spin was a matter of actual measurement, which could be repeated over and over and on which all agreed. The proton-electron theory was only a theory. It was therefore the latter that was questioned.

What was to be done?

Suppose it is wrong to count protons and electrons inside the nucleus as separate particles. Was it possible that an electron and a proton, forced into the close confinement of the atomic nucleus might, by the force of mutual attraction, become so intimately connected as to count as a single particle. One of the first to suggest this, as far back as 1920, was Rutherford.

Such a proton-electron combination would be electrically neutral and in 1921 the American chemist William Draper Harkins used the term *neutron* as a name for it.

If we look at the nitrogen-14 nucleus in this way then it is made up, not of 14 protons and 7 electrons, but of 7 protons and 7 proton-electron combinations. Instead of a total of 21 particles, there would be a total of 14; instead of an odd number, there would be an even number. The structure would now account for the nuclear spin.

But could such a revised theory of nuclear structure be made to seem plausible? The proton-electron theory seemed to make sense because both protons and electrons were known to exist separately and could be detected. If an intimate proton-electron combination could also exist, ought it not exist (or be made to exist) outside the nucleus and ought it not be detected as an isolated particle?

Discovery of the Neutron

Throughout the 1920's scientists searched for the neutron but without success.

One of the troubles was that the particle was electrically neutral. Subatomic particles could be detected in a variety of ways, but every single way makes use of their electric charge. The electric charge of a speeding subatomic particle either repels electrons or attracts them. In either case, electrons are knocked off atoms that are encountered by the speeding subatomic particle.

The atoms with electrons knocked off are now positively charged ions. Droplets of water vapor can form about these ions, or a bubble of gas can form, or a spark of light can be seen. The droplets, the bubbles, and the light can all be detected one way or another and the path of the subatomic particle could be followed by the trail of ions it left behind. Gamma rays, though they carry no charge, are a wave form capable of ionizing atoms.

All the particles and rays that can leave a detectable track of ions behind are called *ionizing radiation* and these are easy to detect.

The hypothetical proton-electron combination, however, which was neither a wave form nor a charged particle was not expected to be able to ionize atoms. It would wander among the atoms without either attracting or repelling electrons and would therefore leave the atomic structure intact. Its pathway could not be followed. In short, then, the neutron was, so to speak, invisible, and the search for it seemed a lost cause. And until it was found, the proton-electron theory of nuclear structure, whatever its obvious deficiencies with respect to nuclear spin, remained the only one to work with.

Then came 1930. The German physicist Walther Wilhelm Georg Bothe and a co-worker, H. Becker, were bombarding the light metal beryllium with alpha particles. Ordinarily, they might expect protons to be knocked out of it, but in this case no protons appeared. They detected some sort of radiation because something was creating certain effects while the alpha particles were bombarding the beryllium but not after the bombardment ceased.

To try to determine something about the properties of this radiation, Bothe and Becker tried putting objects in the way of the radiation. They found the radiation to be remarkably penetrating. It even passed through several centimeters of lead. The only form of radiation that was known at that time to come out of bombarded matter with the capacity of penetrating a thick layer of lead was gamma rays. Bothe and Becker, therefore, decided they had produced gamma rays and reported this.

In 1932 the Joliot-Curies repeated the Bothe-Becker work and got the same results. However, among the objects they placed in the path of the new radiation, they included paraffin, which is made up of the light atoms of carbon and hydrogen. To their surprise, protons were knocked out of the paraffin.

Gamma rays had never been observed to do this, but the Joliot-Curies could not think what else the radiation might be. They simply reported that they had discovered gamma rays to be capable of a new kind of action.

Not so claimed the English physicist James Chadwick. In

that same year he maintained that a gamma ray, which possessed no mass, simply lacked the momentum to hurl a proton out of its place in the atom. Even an electron was too light to do so. (It would be like trying to knock a baseball off the ground and into the air by hitting it with a ping-pong ball.)

Any radiation capable of knocking a proton out of an atom had to consist of particles that were themselves pretty massive. And if one argued like that, then it seemed that the radiation first observed by Bothe and Becker had to be the long-sought-for proton-electron combination. Chadwick used Harkins' term, neutron, for it and made it official. He gets the credit for the discovery of the neutron.

Chadwick managed to work out the mass of the neutron from his experiments and by 1934 it was quite clear that the neutron was more massive than the proton. The best modern data have the mass of the proton set at 1.007825, and that of the neutron just a trifle greater at 1.008665.

The fact that the neutron was just about as massive as the proton was to be expected if the neutron were a proton-electron combination. It was also not surprising that the isolated neutron eventually breaks up, giving up an electron and becoming a proton. Out of any large number of neutrons, half have turned into protons in about 12 minutes.

Nevertheless, although in some ways we can explain the neutron by speaking of it as though it were a proton-electron combination, it really is not. A neutron has a spin of ½ while a proton-electron combination would have a spin of either 0 or 1. The neutron, therefore, must be treated as a single uncharged particle.

The Proton-Neutron Theory

As soon as the neutron was discovered, the German physicist Werner Karl Heisenberg revived the notion that the nucleus must be made up of protons and neutrons, rather than protons and electrons. It was very easy to switch from the latter theory to the former, if one simply remembered to pair the electrons thought to be in the nucleus with protons and give the name neutrons to these combinations.

Thus, the helium-4 nucleus, rather than being made up of 4 protons and 2 electrons, was made up of 2 protons and 2 proton-electron combinations; or 2 protons and 2 neutrons. In the same way the oxygen-16 nucleus instead of being made up of 16 protons and 8 electrons, would be made up of 8 protons and 8 neutrons.

The proton-neutron theory would account for mass numbers and atomic numbers perfectly well. If a nucleus were made up of x protons and y neutrons, then the atomic number would be equal to x and the mass number to $x + y$. (It is now possible to define the mass number of a nucleus in modern terms. It is the number of protons plus neutrons in the nucleus.)

The proton-neutron theory of nuclear structure could account for isotopes perfectly well, too. Consider the 3 oxygen isotopes, oxygen-16, oxygen-17, and oxygen-18. The first would have a nucleus made up of 8 protons and 8 neutrons; the second, one of 8 protons and 9 neutrons; and the third, one of 8 protons and 10 neutrons. In each case the atomic number is 8. The mass numbers however would be 16, 17, and 18, respectively.

In the same way uranium-238 would have a nucleus built of 92 protons and 146 neutrons, while uranium-235 would have one of 92 protons and 143 neutrons.

By the new theory, can we suppose that it is neutrons rather than electrons that somehow hold the protons together against their mutual repulsion, and that more and more neutrons are required to do this as the nucleus grows more massive? At first the number of neutrons required is roughly equal to the number of protons. The helium-4 nucleus contains 2 protons and 2 neutrons, the carbon-12 nucleus contains 6 protons and 6 neutrons, the oxygen-16 nucleus contains 8 protons and 8 neutrons, and so on.

For more complicated nuclei, additional neutrons are needed. In vanadium-51, the nucleus contains 23 protons and 28 neutrons, five more than an equal amount. In bismuth-209, it is 83 protons and 126 neutrons, 43 more than an equal amount. For still more massive nuclei containing a larger number of protons, no amount of neutrons is sufficient to keep the assembly stable. The more massive nuclei are all radioactive.

The manner of radioactive breakdown fits the theory, too. Suppose a nucleus gives off an alpha particle. The alpha particle is a helium nucleus made up of 2 protons and 2 neutrons. If a nucleus loses an alpha particle, its mass number should decline by 4 and its atomic number by 2, and that is what happens.

Suppose a nucleus gives off a beta particle. For a moment, that might seem puzzling. If the nucleus contains only protons and neutrons and no electrons, where does the beta particle come from? Suppose we consider the neutrons as proton-electron combinations. Within many nuclei, the neutrons are quite stable and do not break up as they do in isolation. In the case of certain nuclei, however, they do break up.

Thus the thorium-234 nucleus is made up of 90 protons and 144 neutrons. One of these neutrons might be viewed as breaking up to liberate an electron and leaving behind an unbound proton. If a beta particle leaves then, the number of neutrons decreases by one and the number of protons increases by one. The thorium-234 nucleus (90 protons, 144 neutrons) becomes a protactinium-234 nucleus (91 protons, 143 neutrons).

In short, the proton-neutron theory of nuclear structure could explain all the observed facts just as well as the proton-electron theory, and could explain the nuclear spins, which the proton-electron theory could not. What's more, the isolated neutron had been discovered.

The proton-neutron theory was therefore accepted and remains accepted to this day.

The Nuclear Interaction

In one place, and only one, did the proton-neutron theory seem a little weaker than the proton-electron theory. The electrons in the nucleus were thought to act as a kind of glue holding together the protons.

But the electrons were gone. There were no negative charges at all inside the nucleus, only the positive charges of the proton, plus the uncharged neutron. As many as 83 positive charges were to be found (in the bismuth-209 nucleus) squeezed together and yet not breaking apart.

In the absence of electrons, what kept the protons clinging together?

Was it possible that the electrical repulsion between 2 protons is replaced by an attraction if those protons were pushed together closely enough? Can there be both an attraction *and* a repulsion, with the former the more important at very short range? If this were so, that hypothetical attraction would have to have two properties. First, it would have to be extremely strong—strong enough to overcome the repulsion of two positive charges at very close quarters. Secondly, it would have to be short-range, for no attractive force between protons of any kind was ever detected outside the nucleus.

In addition, this short-range attraction would have to involve the neutron. The hydrogen-1 nucleus was made up of a single proton, but all nuclei containing more than 1 proton had to contain neutrons also to be stable, and only certain numbers of neutrons.

Until the discovery of the neutron, only two kinds of forces, or *interactions,* were known in the universe. These were the *gravitational interaction* and the *electromagnetic interaction.* The electromagnetic interaction was much the stronger of the two—trillions and trillions and trillions of times as strong as the gravitational attraction.

The electromagnetic attraction, however, includes both attraction (between opposite electric charges or between opposite magnetic poles) and repulsion (between like electric charges or magnetic poles). In ordinary bodies, the attractions and repulsions usually cancel each other entirely or nearly entirely, leaving very little of one or the other to be detected as surplus. The gravitational interaction, however, includes only attraction and this increases with mass. By the time you have gigantic masses such as the earth or the sun, the gravitational interaction between them and other bodies is also gigantic.

Both the gravitational and electromagnetic interactions are long-range. The intensity of each interaction declines with distance but only as the square of the distance. If the distance between earth and sun were doubled, the gravitational interaction would still be one-fourth what it is now. If the distance were increased ten times, the interaction would still be 1/(10 × 10) or 1/100 what it is now. It is for this reason that gravitational and electromagnetic interactions can make themselves felt over millions of miles of space.

But now, with the acceptance of the proton-neutron theory of nuclear structure, physicists began to suspect the existence of a third interaction—a *nuclear interaction*—much stronger than the electromagnetic interaction, perhaps 130 times as strong. Furthermore, the nuclear interaction had to decline very rapidly with distance much more rapidly than the electromagnetic interaction did.

In that case, protons in virtual contact, as within the nucleus, would attract each other, but if the distance between them was increased sufficiently to place one outside the nucleus, the nuclear interaction would decrease in intensity to less than the electromagnetic repulsion. The proton would now be repelled by the positive charge of the nucleus and would go flying away. That is why atomic nuclei have to be so small; it is only when they are so tiny that the nuclear interaction can hold them together.

In 1932 Heisenberg tried to work out how these interactions might come into being. He suggested that attractions and repulsions were the result of particles being constantly and rapidly exchanged by the bodies experiencing the attractions and repulsions. Under some conditions, these *exchange particles* moving back and forth very rapidly between two bodies might force those bodies apart; under other conditions they might pull those bodies together.

In the case of the electromagnetic interaction, the exchange particles seemed to be *photons,* wave packets that made up gamma rays, X rays, or even ordinary light (all of which are examples of *electromagnetic radiation*). The gravitational interaction would be the result of exchange particles called *gravitons.* (In 1969, there were reports that gravitons had actually been detected.)

Both the photon and the graviton have zero mass and there is a connection between that and the fact that electromagnetic interaction and gravitational interaction decline only slowly with distance. For a nuclear interaction, which declines very rapidly with distance, any exchange particle would have to have mass.

In 1935 the Japanese physicist Hideki Yukawa worked out in considerable detail the theory of such exchange particles in order to decide what kind of properties the one involved in the nuclear interaction would have. He decided it ought to have a mass about 250 times that of an electron, which would make it about $1/7$ as massive as a proton. Since this mass is intermediate between that of an electron and proton, such particles eventually came to be called *mesons* from a Greek word meaning *intermediate*.

Once Yukawa published his theory, the search was on for the hypothetical mesons. Ideally, if they existed within the nucleus, shooting back and forth between protons and neutrons, there ought to be some way of knocking them out of the nucleus and studying them in isolation. Unfortunately, the bombarding particles at the disposal of physicists in the 1930's possessed far too little energy to knock mesons out of nuclei, assuming they were there in the first place.

There was one way out. In 1911 the Austrian physicist Victor Francis Hess had discovered that earth was bombarded from every side by *cosmic rays*. These consisted of speeding atomic nuclei (*cosmic particles*) of enormous energies—in some cases, billions of times as intense as any energies available through particles produced by mankind. If a cosmic particle of sufficient energy struck an atomic nucleus in the atmosphere, it might knock mesons out of it.

In 1936 the American physicists Carl David Anderson and Seth Henry Neddermeyer, studying the results of cosmic-particle bombardment of matter, detected the existence of particles of intermediate mass. This particle turned out to be lighter than Yukawa had predicted; it was only about 207 times as massive as an electron. Much worse, it lacked other properties that Yukawa had predicted. It did not interact with the nucleus in the manner expected.

In 1947, however, the English physicist Cecil Frank Powell and his co-workers, also studying cosmic-particle bombardment, located another intermediate-sized body, which had the right mass and all the other appropriate properties to fit Yuka-wa's theories.

Anderson's particle was called a *mu-meson*, soon abbreviated to *muon*. Powell's particle was called a *pi-meson*, soon abbreviated to *pion*. With the discovery of the pion, Yukawa's theory was nailed down and any lingering doubt as to the validity of the proton-neutron theory vanished.

(Actually, it turns out that there are two forces. The one with the pion as exchange particle is the *strong nuclear interaction*. Another, involved in beta particle emission, for instance, is a *weak interaction*, much weaker than the electromagnetic but stronger than the gravitational.)

The working out of the details of the strong nuclear interaction explains further the vast energies to be found resulting from nuclear reactions. Ordinary chemical reactions, with the electron shifts that accompany them, involve the electromagnetic interaction only. Nuclear energy, with the shifts of the particles inside the nucleus, involves the much stronger nuclear interaction.

Neutron Bombardment

As soon as neutrons were discovered, it seemed to physicists that they had another possible bombarding particle of extraordinary properties. Since the neutron lacked any electric charge, it could not be repelled by either electrons on the outside of the atoms or by the nuclei at the center. The neutron was completely indifferent to the electromagnetic attraction and it just moved along in a straight line. If it happened to be headed toward a nucleus it would strike it no matter how heavy a charge that nucleus might have and very often it would, as a result, induce a nuclear reaction where a proton would not have been able to.

To be sure, it seemed just at first that there was a disadvantage to the neutron's lack of charge. It could not be accelerated directly by any device since that always depended on electromagnetic interaction to which the neutron was impervious.

There was one way of getting around this and this was explained in 1935 by the American physicist J. Robert Oppenheimer and by his student Melba Phillips.

Use is made here of the nucleus of the hydrogen-2 (deuterium) nucleus. That nucleus, often called a *deuteron*, is made up of 1 proton plus 1 neutron and has a mass number of 2 and an atomic number of 1. Since it has a unit positive charge, it can be accelerated just as an isolated proton can be.

Suppose, then, that a deuteron is accelerated to a high energy and is aimed right at a positively charged nucleus. That nucleus repels the deuteron, and it particularly repels the proton part. The nuclear interaction that holds together a single proton and a single neutron is comparatively weak as nuclear interactions go, and the repulsion of the nucleus that the deuteron is approaching may force the proton out of the deuteron altogether. The proton veers off, but the neutron, unaffected, keeps right on going and, with all the energy it had gained as part of the deuteron acceleration, smashes into the nucleus.

Within a few months of their discovery, energetic neutrons were being used to bring about nuclear reactions.

Actually, though, physicists didn't have to worry about making neutrons energetic. They had needed to work with positively charged particles such as protons and alpha particles. These charged particles had to be energetic to overcome the repulsion of the nucleus and to smash into it with enough force to break it up. Neutrons, however, didn't have to overcome any repulsion. No matter how little energy they had, if they were correctly aimed (and some always were, through sheer chance) they would approach and strike the nucleus.

In fact, the more slowly they travelled, the longer they would stay in the vicinity of a nucleus and the more likely they were to be captured by some nearby nucleus through the attraction of the nuclear interaction. The influence of the nucleus in capturing the neutron was greater the slower the neutron, so that it was almost as though the nucleus were larger and easier to hit for a slow neutron than a fast one. Eventually, physicists began to speak of *nuclear cross sections* and to say that particular nuclei had a cross section of such and such a size for this bombarding particle or that.

The effectiveness of slow neutrons was discovered in 1934 by the Italian-American physicist Enrico Fermi.

Enrico Fermi and Niels Bohr

Of course, there was the difficulty that neutrons couldn't be slowed down once they were formed, and formed they generally had too much energy (according to the new way of looking at things). They couldn't be slowed down by electromagnetic methods—but there were other ways.

A neutron didn't always enter a nucleus that it encountered. Sometimes, if it struck the nucleus a hard, glancing blow, it bounced off. If the nucleus struck by the neutron is many times as massive as the neutron, the neutron bounced off with all its speed practically intact. On the other hand, if the neutron hits a nucleus not very much more massive than itself, the nucleus rebounds and absorbs some of the energy, so that the neutron bounces away with less energy than it had. If the neutron rebounds from a number of comparatively light nuclei, it eventually loses virtually all its energy and finally moves about quite slowly, possessing no more energy than the atoms that surround it.

(You can encounter this situation in ordinary life in the case of billiard balls. A billiard ball, colliding with a cannon ball, will just bounce, moving just as rapidly afterward as before, though in a different direction. If a billiard ball strikes another billiard ball, it will set the target ball moving and bounce off itself with less speed.)

The energy of the molecules in the atmosphere depends on temperature. Neutrons that match that energy and have the ordinary quantity to be expected at room temperature are called *thermal* (from a Greek word meaning *heat*) neutrons. The comparatively light nuclei against which the neutrons bounce and slow down are *moderators* because they moderate the neutron's energy.

Fermi and his co-workers were the first to moderate neutrons, produce thermal neutrons, and use them, in 1935, to bombard nuclei. He quickly noted how large nuclear cross sections became when thermal neutrons were the bombarding particles.

It might seem that hope could now rise in connection with the practical use of energy derived from nuclear reactions. Neutrons could bring about nuclear reactions, even when they themselves possessed very little energy, so output might conceivably be more than input for each neutron that struck. Furthermore, because of the large cross sections involved, thermal neutrons missed far less frequently than high-energy charged particles did.

But there was a catch. Before neutrons could be used, they had to be produced; and in order to produce neutrons they had to be knocked out of nuclei by bombardment with high-energy protons or some other such method. The energy formed by the neutrons was at first never more than the tiniest fraction of the energies that went into forming the neutrons in the first place. It was as though you could light a candle with a single match, but if you had to look through 300,000 useless pieces of wood before you found a match, the candle would be impractical.

Even with the existence of neutron bombardment, involving low energy and high cross section, Rutherford could, with justice, continue to feel until his death in 1937 that nuclear energy would never be made available for practical use.

And yet, among the experiments that Fermi was trying in 1934 was one sending his neutrons crashing into uranium atoms. Neither Rutherford nor Fermi had any way of knowing that this, finally, was the route to the unimaginable.

7

NUCLEAR FISSION

New Elements

In his experiments Fermi had found that slow neutrons, which had very little energy, were easily absorbed by atomic nuclei—more easily than fast neutrons were absorbed, and certainly more easily than charged particles were.

Often the neutron was simply absorbed by the nucleus. Since the neutron has a mass number of 1 and an atomic number of 0 (because it is uncharged), a nucleus that absorbs a neutron remains an isotope of the same element, but increases its mass number.

For instance, suppose that neutrons are used to bombard hydrogen-1, which then captures one of the neutrons. From a single proton, it will become a proton plus a neutron; from hydrogen-1, it will become hydrogen-2. A new nucleus formed in this way will be at a higher energy and that energy is emitted in the form of a gamma ray.

Sometimes the more massive isotope that is formed through neutron absorption is stable, as hydrogen-2 is. Sometimes it is not, but is radioactive instead. Because it has added a neutron, it has too many neutrons for stability. The best way of adjusting the matter is to emit a beta particle (electron). This converts one of the neutrons into a proton. The mass number stays the same but the atomic number increases by one.

The element rhodium, for example, which has an atomic number of 45, has only 1 stable isotope, with a mass number of 103. If rhodium-103 (45 protons, 58 neutrons) absorbs a neutron, it becomes rhodium-104 (45 protons, 59 neutrons), which is not stable. Rhodium-104 emits a beta particle, changing a neutron to a proton so that the nuclear combination becomes

46 protons and 58 neutrons. This is palladium-104, which is stable.

As another example, indium-115 (49 protons, 66 neutrons) absorbs a neutron and becomes indium-116 (49 protons, 67 neutrons), which gives off a beta particle and becomes tin-116 (50 protons, 66 neutrons), which is stable.

There are over 100 isotopes that will absorb neutrons and end by becoming an isotope of an element one higher in the atomic number scale. Fermi observed a number of these cases.

Having done so, he was bound to ask what would happen if uranium were bombarded with neutrons. Would its isotopes also be raised in atomic number—in this case from 92 to 93? If that were so it would be very exciting, for uranium had the highest atomic number in the entire scale. Nobody had ever discovered any sample of element number 93, but perhaps it could be formed in the laboratory.

In 1934, therefore, Fermi bombarded uranium with neutrons in the hope of obtaining atoms of element 93. Neutrons were absorbed and whatever was formed did give off beta particles, so element 93 should be there. However, four different kinds of beta particles (different in their energy content) were given off and the matter grew very confusing. Fermi could not definitely identify the presence of atoms of element 93 and neither could anyone else for several years. Other things turned up, however, which were even more significant.

Before going on to these other things, however, it should be mentioned that undoubtedly element 93 was formed even though Fermi couldn't clearly demonstrate the fact. In 1939 the American physicists Edwin Mattison McMillan and Philip Hauge Abelson, after bombarding uranium atoms with slow neutrons, were able to identify element 93. Since uranium had originally been named for the planet, Uranus, the new element beyond uranium was eventually named for the planet Neptune, which lay beyond Uranus. Element 93 is therefore called *neptunium*.

What happened was exactly what was expected. Uranium-238 (92 protons, 146 neutrons) added a neutron to become uranium-239 (92 protons, 147 neutrons), which emitted a beta particle to become neptunium-239 (93 protons, 146 neutrons).

In fact, neptunium-239 also emitted a beta particle so it ought to become an isotope of an element even higher in the atomic number scale. This one, element 94, was named *plutonium* after Pluto, the planet beyond Neptune. The isotope, plutonium-239, formed from neptunium-239, was only feebly radioactive, however, and it was not clearly identified until 1941.

The actual discovery of the element plutonium came the year before, however, when neptunium-238 was formed. It emitted a beta particle and became plutonium-238, an isotope that was radioactive enough to be easily detected and identified by Glenn Theodore Seaborg, and his co-workers, who completed McMillan's experiments when he was called away to other defense research.

Neptunium and plutonium were the first *transuranium elements* to be produced in the laboratory, but they weren't the last. Over the next 30 years, isotopes were formed that contained more and more protons in the nucleus and therefore had higher and higher atomic numbers.

A number of these new elements have been named for some of the scientists important in the history of nuclear research. Element 96 is *curium,* named for Pierre and Marie Curie; element 99 is *einsteinium* for Albert Einstein; and element 100 is *fermium* for Enrico Fermi.

Element 101 is *mendelevium* for the Russian chemist Dmitri Mendeléev, who early in 1869 was the first to arrange the elements in a reasonable and useful order. Element 103 is *lawrencium* for Ernest O. Lawrence. *Rutherfordium* for Ernest Rutherford has been proposed for element 104.

And *hahnium* for Otto Hahn, a German physical chemist whose contribution we will come to shortly, has been proposed for element 105.

Neptunium, however, was not the first new element to be created in the laboratory. In the early 1930's, there were still two elements with fairly low atomic numbers that had never been discovered. These were the elements with atomic numbers 43 and 61.

In 1937, though, molybdenum (atomic number 42) had been bombarded with neutrons in Lawrence's laboratory in the

United States. It might contain small quantities of element 43 as a result. The Italian physicist Emilio Segrè, who had worked with Fermi, obtained a sample of the bombarded molybdenum and indeed obtained indications of the presence of element 43. It was the first new element to be manufactured by artificial means and was called *technetium* from the Greek word for *artificial*.

The technetium isotope that was formed was radioactive. Indeed, all the technetium isotopes are radioactive. Element 61, discovered in 1945 and named *promethium,* also has no stable isotopes. Technetium and promethium are the only elements with atomic numbers less than 84 that do not have even a single stable isotope.

The Discovery of Fission

But let us get back to the bombardment of uranium with neutrons research that Fermi had begun. After he had reported his work, other physicists repeated it and also got a variety of beta particles and were also unable to decide what was going on.

One way to tackle the problem was to add to the system some stable element that was chemically similar to the tiny traces of radioactive isotopes that might be produced through the bombardment of uranium. Afterwards the stable element could probably be separated out of the mixture and the trace of radioactivity would, it was hoped, be carried along with it. The stable element would be a *carrier*.

Among those working on the problem were Otto Hahn and his Austrian co-worker, the physicist Lise Meitner. Among the potential carriers they added to the system was the element barium which has an atomic number of 56. They found that a considerable quantity of the radioactivity did indeed accompany the barium when they separated that element out of the system.

A natural conclusion was that the isotopes producing the radioactivity belonged to an element that was chemically very similar to barium. Suspicion fell at once on radium (atomic number 88), which was very like barium indeed as far as chemical properties were concerned.

Lise Meitner, who was Jewish, found it difficult to work in Germany, however; for it was then under the rule of the strongly anti-Semitic Nazi regime. In March 1938 Germany occupied Austria, which became part of the German realm. Meitner was no longer protected by her Austrian citizenship and had to flee the country to Stockholm, Sweden. Hahn remained in Germany and continued working on the problem with the German physical chemist Fritz Strassman.

Although the supposed radium, which possessed the radioactivity, was very like barium in chemical properties, the two were not entirely identical. There were ways of separating them, and Hahn and Strassman busied themselves in trying to accomplish this in order to isolate the radioactive isotopes, concentrate them, and study them in detail. Over and over again, however, they failed to separate the barium and the supposed radium.

Slowly, it began to seem to Hahn that the failure to separate the barium and the radioactivity meant that the isotopes to which the radioactivity belonged had to be so much like barium as to be nothing else *but* barium. He hesitated to say so, however, because it seemed unbelievable.

If the radioactive isotopes included radium, that was conceivable. Radium had an atomic number of 88, only four less than uranium's 92. You could imagine that a neutron being absorbed by a uranium nucleus might make the latter so unstable as to cause it to emit 2 alpha particles and become radium. Barium, however, had an atomic number of 56, only a little over half that of uranium. How could a uranium nucleus be made to turn into a barium nucleus unless it more or less broke in half? Nothing like that had ever been observed before and Hahn hesitated to suggest it.

While he was nerving himself to do so, however, Lise Meitner, in Stockholm, receiving reports of what was being done in Hahn's laboratory and thinking about it, decided that unheard-of or not, there was only one explanation. The uranium nucleus *was* breaking in half.

Actually, when one stopped to think of it (after getting over the initial shock) it wasn't so unbelievable at that. The nuclear force is so short-range, it barely reaches from end to end of a large nucleus like that of uranium. Left to itself, it holds together most of the time, but with the added energy of an entering neutron, we might imagine shock waves going through it and turning the nucleus into something like a quivering drop of liquid. Sometimes the uranium nucleus recovers, keeps the neutron, and then goes on to beta-particle emission. And sometimes the nucleus stretches to the point where the nuclear force doesn't quite hold it together. It becomes a dumbbell shape and then the electromagnetic repulsion of the two halves (both positively charged) breaks it apart altogether.

It doesn't break into equal halves. Nor does it always break at exactly the same place, so that there were a number of different fragments possible (which was why there was so much confusion). Still, one of the more common ways in which it might break would be into barium and krypton. (Their respective atomic numbers, 56 and 36, would add up to 92.)

Meitner and her nephew, Otto Robert Frisch, who was in Copenhagen, Denmark, prepared a paper suggesting that this was what was happening. It was published in January 1939. Frisch passed it on to the Danish physicist Niels Bohr with whom he was working. The American biologist William Archibald Arnold, who was also working in Copenhagen at the time, suggested that the splitting of the uranium nucleus into halves be called *fission*, the term used for the division-in-two of living cells. The name stuck.

In January 1939, just about the time Meitner and Frisch's paper was published, Bohr had arrived in the United States to attend a conference of physicists. He carried the news of fission with him. The other physicists attending the conference heard the news and in a high state of excitement at once set about studying the problem. Within a matter of weeks, the fact of uranium fission was confirmed over and over.

One striking fact about uranium fission was the large amount of energy it released. In general, when a very massive nucleus is converted to a less massive one, energy is released because of the change in the mass defect, as Aston had shown in the 1920's. When the uranium nucleus breaks down through the ordinary radioactive processes to become a less massive lead nucleus, energy is given off accordingly. When, however, it breaks in two to become the much less massive nuclei of barium and krypton (or others in that neighborhood) much more energy is given off.

It quickly turned out that uranium fission gave off something like ten times as much nuclear energy per nucleus than did any other nuclear reaction known at the time.

Even so, the quantity of energy released by uranium fission was only a tiny fraction of the energy that went into the preparation of the neutrons used to bring about the fission, if each neutron that struck a uranium atom brought about a single fission of that one atom.

But fission was much more than this.

The Nuclear Chain Reaction

Earlier in this history, we discussed chain reactions involving chemical energy. A small bit of energy can ignite a chemical reaction that would produce more than enough energy to ignite a neighboring section of the system, which would in turn produce still more—and so on, and so on. In this way the flame of a single match could start a fire in a leaf that would burn down an entire forest, and the energy given off by the burning forest would be enormously higher than the initial energy of the match flame.

Might there not be such a thing as a *nuclear chain reaction?* Could one initiate a nuclear reaction that would produce something that would initiate more of the same that would produce something that would initiate still more of the same and so on?

In that case, a nuclear reaction, once started, would continue of its own accord, and in return for the trifling investment that would serve to start it—a single neutron, perhaps—a vast amount of breakdowns would result with the delivery of a vast amount of energy. Even if it were necessary to expend quite a bit of energy to produce the one neutron that would start the chain reaction, one would end with an enormous profit.

What's more, since the nuclear reaction would spread from nucleus to nucleus with millionths-of-a-second intervals, there would be, in a very brief time, so many nuclei breaking down

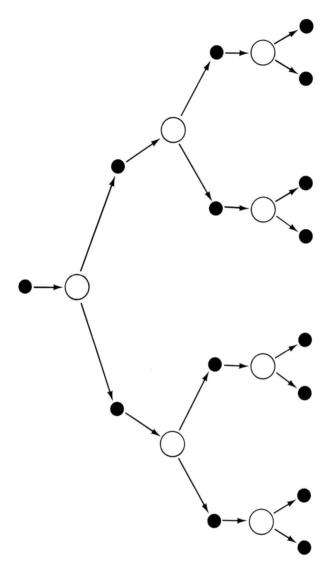

Nuclear fission of uranium: a neutron hits the nucleus of an atom of uranium. The neutron splits the nucleus into two parts and creates huge amounts of energy in the form of heat. At the same time other neutrons are released from the splitting nucleus and these continue the fission process in a chain reaction.

that there would be a vast explosion. The explosion was sure to be millions of times as powerful as ordinary chemical explosions involving the same quantity of exploding material, since the latter used only the electromagnetic interaction, while the former used the much stronger nuclear interaction.

The first to think seriously of such a nuclear chain reaction was the Hungarian physicist Leo Szilard. He was working in Germany in 1933 when Adolf Hitler came to power and, since he was Jewish, he left and went to Great Britain. There, in 1934, he considered certain new types of nuclear reactions that had been discovered.

In these, it sometimes happened that a fast neutron might strike a nucleus with sufficient energy to cause it to emit 2 neutrons. In that way the nucleus, absorbing 1 neutron and emitting 2, would become a lighter isotope of the same element.

But what would happen if each of the 2 neutrons that emerged from the original target nucleus struck new nuclei and forced the emission of a pair of neutrons from each? There would now be a total of 4 neutrons flying about and if each struck new nuclei there would next be 8 neutrons and so on. From the initial investment of a single neutron there might soon be countless billions initiating nuclear reactions.

Szilard, fearing the inevitability of war and fearing further that the brutal leaders of Germany might seek and use such a nuclear chain reaction as a weapon in warfare, secretly applied for a patent on a device intending to make use of such a nuclear chain reaction. He hoped to turn it over to the British Government, which might then use its possession as a way of restraining the Nazis and keeping the peace.

However, it wouldn't have worked. It took the impact of a very energetic neutron to bring about the emission of 2 neutrons. The neutrons that then emerged from the nucleus simply didn't have enough energy to keep things going. (It was like trying to make wet wood catch fire.)

But what about uranium fission? Uranium fission was initiated by slow neutrons. What if uranium fission also produced neutrons as well as being initiated by a neutron? Would not the neutrons produced serve to initiate new fissions that would produce new neutrons and so on endlessly?

101

It seemed very likely that fission produced neutrons and indeed, Fermi, at the conference where fission was first discussed, suggested it at once. Massive nuclei possessed more neutrons per proton than less massive ones did. If a massive nucleus was broken up into 2 considerably less massive ones, there would be a surplus of neutrons. Suppose, for instance, uranium-238 broke down into barium-138 and krypton-86. Barium-138 contains 82 neutrons and krypton-86 50 neutrons for a total of 132. The uranium-238 nucleus, however, contains 146 neutrons.

The uranium fission process was studied at once to see if neutrons were actually given off and a number of different physicists, including Szilard, found that they were.

Now Szilard was faced with a nuclear chain reaction he was certain would work. Only slow neutrons were involved and the individual nuclear breakdowns were far more energetic than anything else that had yet been discovered. If a chain reaction could be started in a sizable piece of uranium, unimaginable quantities of energy would be produced. Just 1 gram of uranium, undergoing complete fission, would deliver the energy derived from the total burning of 3 tons of coal and would deliver that energy in a tiny fraction of a second.

Szilard, who had come to the United States in 1937, clearly visualized the tremendous explosive force of something that would have to be called a *nuclear bomb*. Szilard dreaded the possibility that Hitler might obtain the use of such a bomb through the agency of Germany's nuclear scientists.

Partly through Szilard's efforts, physicists in the United States and in other Western nations opposed to Hitler began a program of voluntary secrecy in 1940, to avoid passing along any hints to Germany. What's more, Szilard enlisted the services of two other Hungarian refugees, the physicists Eugene Paul Wigner and Edward Teller and all approached Einstein, who had also fled Germany and come to America.

Einstein was the most prestigious scientist then living, and it was thought a letter from him to the President of the United States would be most persuasive. Einstein signed such a letter, which explained the possibility of a nuclear bomb and urged that the United States not allow a potential enemy to come into possession of it first.

Largely as a result of this letter, a huge research team was put together in the United States, to which other Western nations also contributed, with but one aim—to develop the nuclear bomb.

The Nuclear Bomb

Although the theory of the nuclear bomb seemed clear and simple, a great many practical difficulties stood in the way. In the first place, if only uranium atoms underwent fission a supply of uranium had at least to be obtained in pure form, for if the neutrons struck nuclei of elements other than uranium, they would simply be absorbed and removed from the system, ending the possibility of a chain reaction. This alone was a heavy task, since there had been so little use for uranium in quantity that there was almost no supply in existence and no experience in how to purify it.

Secondly, the supply of uranium might have to be a large one, for neutrons didn't necessarily enter the first uranium atom they approached. They moved about here and there, making glancing collisions, and travelling quite a distance, perhaps, before striking head-on and entering a nucleus. If in that time they had passed outside the lump of uranium, they were useless.

As the quantity of uranium within which the fission chain reaction was initiated grew larger, more and more of the neutrons produced found a mark and the fission reaction would die out more and more slowly. Finally, at some particular size—the *critical size*—the fission reaction did not die at all, but maintained itself, with enough of the neutrons produced finding their mark to keep the nuclear reaction proceeding at a steady rate. At any greater size the nuclear reaction would accelerate and there would be an explosion.

It wasn't even necessary to send neutrons into the uranium to start the process. In 1941 the Russian physicist Georgii Nikolaevich Flerov found that every once in a while a uranium atom would undergo fission without the introduction of a neutron. Occasionally the random quivering of a nucleus would bring about a shape that the nuclear interaction could not bring back to normal and the nucleus would then break apart. In a gram of ordinary uranium, there is a nucleus undergoing such *spontaneous fission* every two minutes on the average. Therefore, enough uranium need only be brought together to surpass critical size and it will explode within seconds, for the first nucleus that undergoes spontaneous fission will start the chain reaction.

First estimates made it seem that the quantity of uranium needed to reach critical size was extraordinarily great. Fully 99.3% of the metal is uranium-238, however, and, as soon as fission was discovered, Bohr pointed out that there were theoretical reasons for supposing that it was the uranium-235 isotope (making up only 0.7% of the whole) that was the one undergoing fission. Investigation proved him right. Indeed, the uranium-238 nucleus tended to absorb slow neutrons without fission, and to go on to beta-particle production that formed isotopes of neptunium and plutonium. In this way uranium-238 actually interfered with the chain reaction.

In any quantity of uranium, the more uranium-235 present and the less uranium-238, the more easily the chain reaction would proceed and the lower the critical size needed. Vast efforts were therefore made to separate the two isotopes and prepare uranium with a higher than normal concentration of uranium-235 (*enriched uranium*).

Of course, there was no great desire for a fearful explosion to get out of hand while the chain reaction was being studied. Before any bomb could be constructed, the mechanism of the chain reaction would have to be studied. Could a chain reaction capable of producing energy (for useful purposes as well as for bombs) be established? To test this, a quantity of uranium was gathered in the hope that a *controlled* chain reaction of uranium fission could be established. For that purpose, control rods of a substance that would easily absorb neutrons and slow the chain reaction were used. The metal, cadmium, served admirably for this purpose.

Then, too, the neutrons released by fission were pretty energetic. They tended to travel too far too soon and get outside the lump of uranium too easily. To produce a chain reaction that could be studied with some safety, the presence of a moderator was needed. This was a supply of small nuclei that did not absorb neutrons readily, but absorbed some of the energy of collision and slowed down any neutron that struck it. Nuclei such as hydrogen-2, beryllium-9, or carbon-12 were useful moderators. When the neutrons produced by fission were slowed, they travelled a smaller distance before being absorbed in their turn and the critical size would again be reduced.

Toward the end of 1942 the initial stage of the project reached a climax. Blocks of graphite containing uranium metal and uranium oxide were piled up in huge quantities (enriched uranium was not yet available) in order to approach critical size. This took place under the stands of a football stadium at the University of Chicago, with Enrico Fermi (who had come to the United States in 1938) in charge.

The large structure was called an *atomic pile* at first because of the blocks of graphite being piled up. The proper name for such a device, and the one that was eventually adopted, was, however, *nuclear reactor*.

On December 2, 1942, calculations showed that the nuclear reactor was large enough to have reached critical size. The only thing preventing the chain reaction from sustaining itself was the cadmium rods that were inserted here and there in the pile and that were soaking up neutrons.

One by one the cadmium rods were pulled out. The number of uranium atoms undergoing fission each second rose and, finally, at 3:45 p.m., the uranium fission became self-sustaining. It kept going on its own (with the cadmium rods ready to be pushed in if it looked as though it were getting out of hand— something calculations showed was not likely).

News of this success was announced to Washington by a cautious telephone call from Arthur Holly Compton to James Bryant Conant. "The Italian navigator has landed in the new world," said Compton. Conant asked, "How were the natives?" and the answer was, "Very friendly."

This was the day and moment when the world entered the *nuclear age*. For the first time, mankind had constructed a device in which the nuclear energy being given off was greater than the energy poured in. Mankind had tapped the reservoirs of

Subcritical reactor constructed at Argonne National Laboratory with original graphite and uranium used by Dr. Enrico Fermi and his associates in the world's first nuclear reactor.

nuclear energy and could put it to use. Had Rutherford lived but six more years, he would have seen how wrong he was to think it could never be done.

The people of earth remained unaware of what had taken place in Chicago and physicists continued to work toward the development of the nuclear bomb.

Enriched uranium was successfully prepared. Critical sizes were brought low enough to make a nuclear bomb small enough to be carried by plane to some target. Suppose one had two slabs of enriched uranium, each below critical size, but which were above critical size if combined. And suppose an explosive device were added that, at some desired moment, could be set off in such a way that it would drive one slab of enriched uranium against the other. There would be an instant explosion of devastating power. Or suppose the enriched uranium were arranged in loosely packed pieces to begin with so that the flying neutrons were in open air too often to maintain the chain reaction. A properly arranged explosion might compress the uranium into a dense ball. Neutron absorption would become more efficient and again, an explosion would follow.

On July 16, 1945, a device that would result in a nuclear explosion was set up near Alamogordo, New Mexico, with nervous physicists watching from a distance. It worked perfectly; the explosion was tremendous.

By that time Nazi Germany had been defeated, but Japan was still fighting. Two more devices were prepared. After a warning, one was exploded over the Japanese city of Hiroshima on August 6, 1945, and the other over Nagasaki two days later. The Japanese government surrendered and World War II came to an end.

It was with the blast over Hiroshima that the world came to know it was in the nuclear age and that the ferocious weapon of the nuclear bomb existed. (The popular name for it at the time was *atomic bomb* or *A-bomb*.)

During the war, German scientists may have been trying to develop a nuclear bomb, but, if so, they had not yet succeeded at the time Germany met its final defeat. Soviet physicists, under Igor Vasilievich Kurchatov, were also working on the problem. The dislocation of the war, which inflicted much more

damage on the Soviet Union than on the United States, kept the Soviet effort from succeeding while it was on. However, since the Soviets were among the victors, they were able to continue after the war.

In 1949 the Soviets exploded their first nuclear bomb. In 1952 the British did the same; in 1960, the French; and in 1964, the Chinese. Although many nuclear bombs have been exploded for test purposes, the two over Hiroshima and Nagasaki have been the only ones used in time of war.

Nor need nuclear bombs be considered as having destructive potential only. There is the possibility that, with proper precautions, they might be used to make excavations, blast out harbors or canals, break up underground rock formations to recover oil or other resources, and in other ways do the work of chemical explosives with far greater speed and economy. It has even been suggested that a series of nuclear bomb explosions might be used to hurl space vehicles forward in voyages away from earth.

Nuclear Reactors

The development of the nuclear chain reaction was not in the direction of bombs only. Nuclear reactors designed for the controlled production of useful energy multiplied in number and in efficiency since Fermi's first *pile*. Many nations now possess them, and they are used for a variety of purposes.

In 1954 the first nuclear submarine the USS *Nautilus* was launched by the United States. Its power was obtained entirely from a nuclear reactor, and it was not necessary for it to rise to the surface at short intervals in order to recharge its batteries. Since then Congress has authorized 118 nuclear-powered submarines, one deep submergence research vehicle, and eleven nuclear-powered surface ships. Of these, 130 ships, 95 submarines, one deep submergence research vehicle, and 4 surface ships are operating and have steamed over 19,000,000 miles. Nuclear submarines have crossed the Arctic Ocean under the ice cover, and have circumnavigated the globe without surfacing.

In 1959 both the Soviet Union and the United States launched nuclear-powered surface vessels. The Soviet ship was the icebreaker, *Lenin,* and the American ship was a merchant vessel, the NS *Savannah,* which is now retired. Other nuclear powered ships belonging to foreign countries are being operated now.

In the 1950's nuclear reactors began to be used as the source of power for the production of electricity for civilian use. The Soviet Union built a small station of this sort in 1954, which had a capacity of 5,000 kilowatts. The British built one of 92,000 kilowatt capacity, which they called Calder Hall. The first American nuclear reactor for civilian use began operation at Shippingport, Pennsylvania, in 1958. It was the first really full-scale civilian nuclear power plant in the world. For the production of electricity for civilian use, there are now in the U.S. 55 nuclear reactors licensed to operate, 73 being built, and 93 ordered.

The world appeared to have far greater sources of energy than had been expected. The *fossil fuels*—coal, oil and natural gas—were being used at such a rate that many speculated that the gas and oil would be gone in decades and the coal in centuries. Was it possible that uranium might now serve as a new source that would last indefinitely?

It was rather disappointing that it was uranium-235 which underwent fission, because that isotope made up only 0.7% of the uranium that existed. If uranium-235 were all we had and all we ever could have, the energy supply of the world would still be rather too limited.

There were other possible *nuclear fuels,* however. There was plutonium-239, which would also fission under neutron bombardment. It had an ordinary half-life (for a radioactive change in which it gave off alpha particles) of 24,300 years, which is long enough to make it easy to handle.

But how can plutonium-239 be formed in sufficient quantities to be useful? After all, it doesn't occur in nature. Surprisingly, that turned out to be easy. Uranium-238 atoms will absorb many of the neutrons that are constantly leaking out of the reactor and will become first neptunium-239 and then plutonium-239. The plutonium, being a different element from the uranium, can be separated from uranium and obtained in useful quantities.

The Shippingport Atomic Power Station (above), the first full-scale, nuclear-electric station built exclusively for civilian needs, provides electricity for the homes and factories of the greater Pittsburgh area. Below are the lights of downtown Pittsburgh.

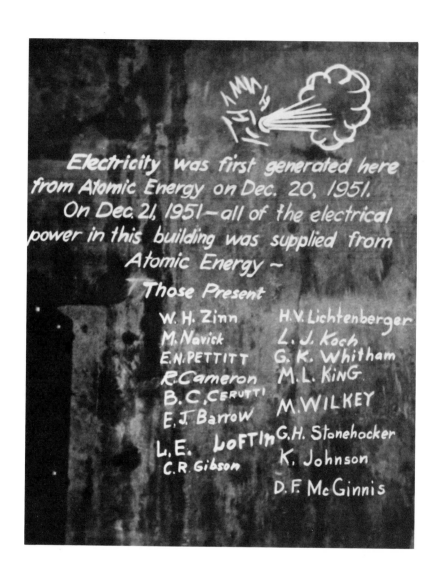

Electricity was first generated here from Atomic Energy on Dec. 20, 1951. On Dec. 21, 1951 — all of the electrical power in this building was supplied from Atomic Energy —

Those Present

W. H. Zinn	H. V. Lichtenberger
M. Navick	L. J. Koch
E. N. PETTITT	G. K. Whitham
R. Cameron	M. L. KiNG
B. C. CERUTTI	M. WILKEY
E. J. Barrow	
L. E. LoFTIn	G. H. Stonehocker
C. R. Gibson	K. Johnson
	D. F. McGinnis

Such a device is called a *breeder reactor* because it breeds fuel. Indeed, it can be so designed to produce more plutonium-239 than the uranium-235 it uses up, so that you actually end up with more nuclear fuel than you started with. In this way, all the uranium on earth (and not just uranium-235) can be considered potential nuclear fuel.

The first breeder reactor was completed at Arco, Idaho, in August 1951, and on December 20 produced the very first electricity on earth to come from nuclear power.

In 1945 Enrico Fermi said, "The country which first develops a breeder reactor will have a great competitive advantage in atomic energy." During the quarter century since Fermi's statement, there have been significant developments in the technology of breeder reactors and a coordinated effort for future breeder development is underway. A major part of this effort has been defined and will be carried out under the direction of the U.S. Energy Research and Development Administration through its Liquid Metal Fast Breeder Reactor Program. The LMFBR Program covers a period of about 20 years and ends in the 1990's with the introduction of commercial nuclear power plants using fast-breeder reactors.

The first U.S. LMFBR demonstration plant will be built and operated under a cooperative arrangement between industrial contractors, utilities, and the Federal Government. The project's estimated cost of $1 billion includes construction, related research and development, and five years of operation. The LMFBR demonstration plant will have a capacity of 350 megawatts and will be located on the Clinch River near Oak Ridge, Tennessee.

In space, as on land and sea, atomic energy promises to pave the way into the future. As payloads grow larger and the energy required to move them around in space increases, the nuclear rocket will greatly increase the propulsion capability of our space vehicles. Electric power generated from radioisotopes or nuclear reactors will continue to become more important as we move farther from the sun, as mission lifetimes in space increase, or as power requirements become greater for more sophisticated payloads.

Another isotope capable of fissioning under neutron bombardment is uranium-233. It does not occur in nature, but was formed in the laboratory by Seaborg and others in 1942. It has a half-life of 162,000 years. It can be formed from naturally occurring thorium-232. Thorium-232 will absorb a neutron to become thorium-233. Then 2 beta particles are given off so that the thorium-233 becomes first protactinium-233 and then uranium-233.

If a thorium shell surrounds a nuclear reactor, fissionable uranium-233 is formed within it and is easily separated from the thorium. In this way, thorium is also added to the list of earth's potential nuclear fuels.

If all the uranium and thorium in the earth's crust (including the thin scattering of those elements through granite, for instance) were available for use, we might get up to 100 times as much energy from it as from all the coal and oil on the planet. Unfortunately, it is very unlikely that we will ever be able to make use of all the uranium and thorium. It is widely and thinly spread through the crustal rocks and much of it could not be extracted without using up more energy than would be supplied by it once isolated.

Another problem rests with the nature of the fission reaction. When the uranium-235 nucleus (or plutonium-239 or uranium-233) undergoes fission, it breaks up into any of a large number of middle-sized nuclei that are radioactive—much more intensely radioactive than the original fuel. (It was from among these *fission products* that isotopes of element 61 were first obtained in 1945. Coming from the nuclear fire, it reminded its discoverers of Prometheus, who stole fire from the sun in the Greek myths, and so it was called *promethium.*)

The fission products still contain energy and some of them can be used in lightweight *nuclear batteries*. Such nuclear batteries were first built in 1954. Some batteries, using plutonium-238 rather than fission products, have been put to use in powering artificial satellites over long periods.

A small proportion of the fission products can be put to profitable use. As the use of nuclear power increases, there will be an accumulation of increasing quantities of nuclear wastes. Nuclear wastes differ from normal industrial wastes in several ways. First, they are radioactive. Second, they occupy a small volume when compared with wastes from fossil fuels. Hundreds of tons of combustion products are produced daily in the operation of a fossil-fuel plant, while a nuclear power plant produces several pounds of highly radioactive fission product wastes each day. Third, the bulk of the nuclear wastes is effectively contained within the fuel while it produces energy. Although there is a slight *exhaust* from the nuclear power plant, essentially all the waste products remain with the unused fuel at the end of power production.

8

NUCLEAR FUSION

The Energy of the Sun

As it happens, though, nuclear fission is not the only route to useful nuclear energy. Aston's studies in the 1920's had shown that it was the middle-sized nuclei that were most tightly packed. Energy would be given off if middle-sized nuclei were produced from either extreme. Not only would energy be formed by the breakup of particularly massive nuclei through fission, but also through the combination of small nuclei to form larger ones (*nuclear fusion*).

In fact, from Aston's studies it could be seen that, mass for mass, nuclear fusion would produce far more energy than nuclear fission. This was particularly true in the conversion of hydrogen to helium; that is, the conversion of the individual protons of 4 separate hydrogen nuclei into the 2-proton−2-neutron structure of the helium nucleus. A gram of hydrogen, undergoing fusion to helium, would deliver some fifteen times as much energy as a gram of uranium undergoing fission.

As early as 1920, the English astronomer Arthur Stanley Eddington had speculated that the sun's energy might be derived from the interaction of subatomic particles. Some sort of nuclear reaction seemed, by then, to be the most reasonable way of accounting for the vast energies constantly being produced by the sun.

The speculation became more plausible with each year. Eddington himself studied the structure of stars, and by 1926 had produced convincing theoretical reasons for supposing that the center of the sun was at enormous densities and temperatures. A temperature of some 15,000,000 to 20,000,000°C seemed to characterize the sun's center.

At such temperatures, atoms could not exist in earthly fashion. Held together by the sun's strong gravitational field, they collided with such energy that all or almost all their electrons were stripped off, and little more than bare nuclei were left. These bare nuclei could approach each other much more closely than whole atoms could (which was why the center of the sun was so much more dense than earthly matter could be). The bare nuclei, smashing together at central-sun temperatures, could cling together and form more complex nuclei. Nuclear reactions brought about by such intense heat (millions of degrees) are called *thermonuclear reactions*.

As the 1920's progressed further studies of the chemical structure of the sun showed it to be even richer in hydrogen than had been thought. In 1929 the American astronomer Henry Norris Russell reported evidence that the sun was 60% hydrogen in volume. (Even this was too conservative; 80% is considered more nearly correct now.) If the sun's energy were based on nuclear reactions at all, then it had to be the result of hydrogen fusion. Nothing else was present in sufficient quantity to be useful as a fuel.

More and more was learned about the exact manner in which nuclei interacted and about the quantity of energy given off in particular nuclear reactions. It became possible to calculate what might be going on inside the sun by considering the densities and temperatures present, the kind and number of different nuclei available, and the quantity of energy that must be produced. In 1938 the German-American physicist Hans Albrecht Bethe and the German astronomer Carl Friedrich von Weizsäcker independently worked out the possible reactions, and hydrogen fusion was shown to be a thoroughly practical way of keeping the sun going.

Thanks to the high rate of energy production by thermonuclear reactions and to the vast quantity of hydrogen in the sun, not only has it been possible for the sun to have been radiating energy for the last 5,000,000,000 years or so, but it will continue to radiate energy in the present fashion for at least 5,000,000,000 years into the future.

Even so, the sheer quantity of what is going on in the sun is staggering in earthly terms. In the sun 650,000,000 tons of hydrogen are converted into helium every second, and in the process each second sees the disappearance of 4,600,000 tons of mass.

Thermonuclear Bombs

Could thermonuclear reactions be made to take place on earth? The conditions that exist in the center of the sun would be extremely difficult to duplicate on the earth, so there was a natural search for any kind of nuclear fusion that would produce similar energies to those going on in the sun but which would be easier to bring about.

There are 3 hydrogen isotopes known to exist. Ordinary hydrogen is almost entirely hydrogen-1, with a nucleus made up of a single proton. Small quantities of hydrogen-2 (deuterium) with a nucleus made up of a proton plus a neutron also exist and such atoms are perfectly stable.

In 1934 Rutherford, along with the Australian physicist Marcus Laurence Elwin Oliphant and the Austrian chemist Paul Harteck sent hydrogen-2 nuclei flying into hydrogen-2 targets and formed hydrogen-3 (also called *tritium* from the Greek word for *third*) with a nucleus made up of a proton plus 2 neutrons. Hydrogen-3 is mildly radioactive.

Hydrogen-2 fuses to helium more easily than hydrogen-1 does and, all things being equal, hydrogen-2 will do so at lower temperatures than hydrogen-1. Hydrogen-3 requires lower temperatures still. But even for hydrogen-3 it still takes millions of degrees.

Hydrogen-3, although the easiest to be forced to undergo fusion, exists only in tiny quantities.

Hydrogen-2, therefore, is the one to pin hopes on especially in conjunction with hydrogen-3. Only 1 atom out of every 6000 hydrogen atoms is hydrogen-2, but that is enough. There exists a vast ocean on earth that is made up almost entirely of water molecules and in each water molecule 2 hydrogen atoms are present. Even if only 1 in 6000 of these hydrogen atoms is deuterium that still means there are about 35,000 billion tons of deuterium in the ocean.

What's more, it isn't necessary to dig for that deuterium or to drill for it. If ocean water is allowed to run through separation plants, the deuterium can be extracted without very much trouble. In fact, for the energy you could get out of it, deuterium from the oceans, extracted by present methods and without allowing for future improvement, would be only one-hundredth as expensive as coal.

The deuterium in the world's ocean, if allowed to undergo fusion little by little, would supply mankind with enough energy to keep us going at the present rate for 500,000,000,000 years. To be sure, to make deuterium fusion practical, it may be necessary to make use of rarer substances such as the light metal lithium. This will place a sharper limit on the energy supply but even if we are careful, fusion would probably supply mankind with energy for as long as mankind will exist.

Then, too, there would seem to be very little danger of hydrogen fusion plants running out of control. Only small quantities of deuterium would be in the process of fusion at any one time. If anything at all went wrong, the deuterium supply could be automatically cut off and the fusion process, with so little involved, would then stop instantly. Moreover, there would be less atomic waste; for the most dangerous products—hydrogen-3 and neutrons—could be easily taken care of.

It seems ideal, but there is a catch. However clear the theory, before a fusion power station can be established some practical method must be found to start the fusion process, which means finding some way for attaining temperatures in the millions of degrees.

One method for obtaining the necessary temperature was known by 1945. An exploding fission bomb would do it. If, somehow, the necessary hydrogen-2 was combined with a fission bomb, the explosion would set off a fusion reaction that would greatly multiply the energy released. You would have in effect a *thermonuclear bomb*. (To the general public, this was commonly known as a *hydrogen bomb* or an *H-bomb*.)

In 1952 the first fusion device was exploded by the United States in the Marshall Islands. Within months, the Soviet Union had exploded one of its own and in time thermonuclear bombs thousands of times as powerful as the first fission bomb over Hiroshima were built and exploded.

All thermonuclear bombs have been exploded only for test purposes. Even testing seems to be dangerous, however, at least if it is carried on in the open atmosphere. The radioactivity liberated spreads over the world and may do slow but cumulative damage.

Controlled Fusion

However effective a fusion bomb may be in liberating vast quantities of energy, it is not what one has in mind when speaking of a fusion power station. The energy of a fusion bomb is released all at once and its only function is that of utter destruction. What is wanted is the production of fusion energy at a low and steady rate—a rate that is under the control of human operators.

The sun, for instance, is a vast fusion furnace 866,000 miles across, but it is a controlled one—even though that control is exerted by the impersonal laws of nature. It releases energy at a very steady and very slow rate. (The rate is not slow in human terms, of course, but stars sometimes do release their energy in a much more cataclysmic fashion. The result is a *supernova* in which for a short time a single star will increase its radiation to as much as a trillion times its normal level.)

The sun (or any star) going at its normal rate is controlled and steady in its output because of the advantage of huge mass. An enormous mass, composed mainly of hydrogen, compresses itself, through its equally enormous gravitational field, into huge densities and temperatures at its center, thus igniting the fusion reaction—while the same gravitational field keeps the sun together against its tendency to expand.

There is, as far as scientists know, no conceivable way of concentrating a high gravitational field in the absence of the required mass, and the creation of controlled fusion on earth must therefore be done without the aid of gravity. Without a huge gravitational force we cannot simultaneously bring about sun-center densities and sun-center temperatures; one or the other must go.

On the whole, it would take much less energy to aim at the temperatures than at the densities and would be much more feasible. For this reason, physicists have been attempting, all through the nuclear age, to heat thin wisps of hydrogen to enormous temperature. Since the gas is thin, the nuclei are farther apart and collide with each other far fewer times per second. To achieve fusion ignition, therefore, temperatures must be considerably higher than those at the center of the sun. In 1944 Fermi calculated that it might take a temperature of 50,000,000° to ignite a hydrogen-3 fusion with hydrogen-2 under earthly conditions, and 400,000,000° to ignite hydrogen-2 fusion alone. To ignite hydrogen-1 fusion, which is what goes on in the sun (at a mere 15,000,000°), physicists would have to raise their sights to beyond the billion-degree mark.

This would make it seem almost essential to use hydrogen-3 in one fashion or another. Even if it can't be prepared in quantity to begin with, it might be formed by neutron bombardment of lithium, with the neutrons being formed by the fusion reaction. In this way, you would start with lithium and hydrogen-2 plus a little hydrogen-3. The hydrogen-3 is formed as fast as it is used up. Although in the end hydrogen is converted to helium in a controlled fusion reaction as in the sun, the individual steps in the reaction under human control are quite different from those in the sun.

Still, even the temperatures required for hydrogen-3 represent an enormous problem, particularly since the temperature must not only be reached, but must be held for a period of time. (You can pass a piece of paper rapidly through a candle flame without lighting it. It must be held in the flame for a short period to give it a chance to heat and ignite.)

The English physicist John David Lawson worked out the requirements in 1957. The time depended on the density of the gas. The denser the gas, the shorter the period over which the temperature had to be maintained. If the gas is about one hundred-thousand times as dense as air, the proper temperature must be held, under the most favorable conditions, for about one thousandth of a second.

There are a number of different ways in which a quantity of hydrogen can be heated to very high temperatures—through

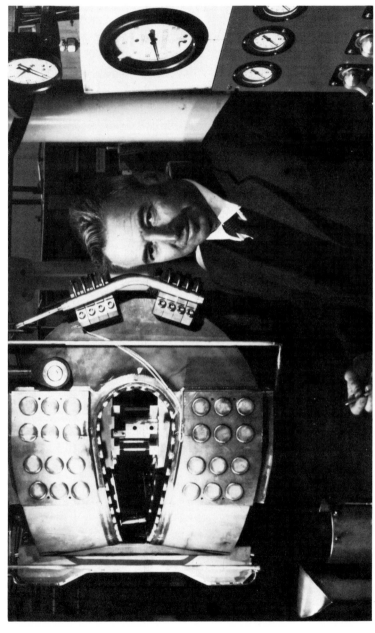

Richard Post, inventor of the Direct Conversion Fusion Reactor, a pioneer in the neutral atomic beam injection approach to producing thermal nuclear plasma in so-called magnetic-mirror containers

electric currents, through magnetic fields, through laser beams and so on. As the temperature goes up into the tens of thousands of degrees, the hydrogen atoms (or any atoms) are broken up into free electrons and bare nuclei. Such a mixture of charged particles is called a *plasma*. Ever since physicists have begun to try to work with very hot gases, with fusion energy in mind, they have had to study the properties of such plasma, and a whole new science of *plasma physics* has come into existence.

But if you do heat a gas to very high temperatures, it will tend to expand and thin out to uselessness. How can such a super-hot gas be confined in a fixed volume without an enormous gravitational field to hold it together.

An obvious answer would be to place it in a container, but no ordinary container of matter will serve to hold the hot gas. You may think this is because the temperature of the gas will simply melt or vaporize whatever matter encloses it. This is not so. Although the gas is at a very high temperature, it is so thin that it has very little total heat. It does not have enough heat to melt the solid walls of a container. What happens instead is that the hot plasma cools down the moment it touches the solid walls and the entire attempt to heat it is ruined.

What's more, if you try to invest the enormous energies required to keep the plasma hot despite the cooling effect of the container walls, then the walls will gradually heat and melt. Nor must one wait for the walls to melt and the plasma to escape before finding the attempt at fusion ruined. Even as the walls heat up they liberate some of their own atoms into the plasma and introduce impurities that will prevent the fusion reaction. Any material container is therefore out of the question.

Fortunately, there is a nonmaterial way of confining plasma. Since plasma consists of a mixture of electrically charged particles, it can experience electromagnetic interactions. Instead of keeping the plasma in a material container, you can surround it by a magnetic field that is designed to keep it in place. Such a magnetic field is not affected by any heat, however great, and cannot be a source of material impurity.

In 1934, the American physicist Willard Harrison Bennett had worked out a theory dealing with the behavior of magnetic fields enclosing plasma. It came to be called the *pinch effect*

Magnetic coils used to confine and compress fusion plasma are visible during modification to the fusion research device.

because the magnetic field pinched the gas together and held it in place.

The first attempt to make use of the pinch effect for confining plasma, with eventual ignition of fusion in mind, was in 1951 by the English physicist Alan Alfred Ware. Other physicists followed, not only in Great Britain, but in the United States and the Soviet Union as well.

The first use of the pinch effect was to confine the plasma in a cylinder. This, however, could not be made to work. The situation was too unstable. The plasma was held momentarily, then writhed and broke up.

Attempts were made to remove the instability. The field was so designed as to be stronger at the ends of the cylinder than elsewhere. The particles in the plasma would stream toward one end or another and would then bounce back producing a so-called *magnetic mirror.*

In 1951 the American physicist Lyman Spitzer, Jr. had worked out the theoretical benefits to be derived from a container twisted into a figure-eight shape. Eventually, such devices were built and called *stellarators* from the Latin word for *star,* because it was hoped that it would produce the conditions that would allow the sort of fusion reactions that went on in stars. All through the 1950's and 1960's, physicists were slowly inching toward their goal, reaching higher and higher temperatures and holding them for longer and longer periods in denser and denser gases.

In 1969 the Soviet Union used a device called *Tokamak-3* (a Russian abbreviation for their phrase for *electric-magnetic*) to keep a supply of hydrogen-2, a millionth as dense as air, in place while heating it to tens of millions of degrees for a hundredth of a second. A little denser, a little hotter, a little longer—and controlled fusion might become possible.

9

BEYOND FUSION

Antimatter

Is there anything that lies beyond fusion?

When hydrogen undergoes fusion and becomes helium, only 0.7% of the original mass of the hydrogen is converted to energy. Is it possible to take a quantity of mass and convert all of it, every bit, to energy? Surely that would be the ultimate energy source. Mass for mass, that would deliver 140 times as much energy as hydrogen fusion would; it would be as far beyond hydrogen fusion as hydrogen fusion is beyond uranium fission.

And, as a matter of fact, total annihilation of matter is conceivable under some circumstances.

In 1928 the English physicist Paul Adrien Maurice Dirac presented a treatment of the electron's properties that made it appear as though there ought also to exist a particle exactly like the electron in every respect except that it would be opposite in charge. It would carry a positive electric charge exactly as large as the electron's negative one.

If the electron is a particle, this suggested positively charged twin would be an *antiparticle*. (The prefix comes from a Greek word meaning *opposite*.)

The proton is *not* the electron's antiparticle. Though a proton carries the necessary positive charge that is exactly as large as the negative charge of the electron, the proton has a much larger mass than the electron has. Dirac's theory required that the antiparticle have the same mass as the particle to which it corresponded.

In 1932 C. D. Anderson was studying the impact of cosmic particles on lead. In the process, he discovered signs of a particle that left tracks exactly like those of an electron, but tracks that curved the wrong way in a magnetic field. This was a sure sign that it had an electric charge opposite to that of the electron. He had, in short, discovered the electron's antiparticle and this came to be called the *positron*.

Positrons were soon detected elsewhere too. Some radioactive isotopes, formed in the laboratory by the Joliot-Curies and by others, were found to emit positive beta particles—positrons rather than electrons. When an ordinary beta particle, or electron, was emitted from a nucleus, a neutron within the nucleus was converted to a proton. When a positive beta particle, a positron, was emitted, the reverse happened—a proton was converted to a neutron.

A positron, however, does not endure long after formation. All about it were atoms containing electrons. It could not move for more than a millionth of a second or so before it encountered one of those electrons. When it did, there was an attraction between the two, since they were of opposite electric charge. Briefly they might circle each other (to form a combination called *positronium*) but only very briefly. Then they collided and, since they were opposites, each cancelled the other.

The process whereby an electron and a positron met and cancelled is called *mutual annihilation*. Not everything was gone, though. The mass, in disappearing, was converted into the equivalent amount of energy, which made its appearance in the form of one or more gamma rays.

(It works the other way, too. A gamma ray of sufficient energy can be transformed into an electron and a positron. This phenomenon, called *pair production,* was observed as early as 1930 but was only properly understood after the discovery of the positron.)

Of course, the mass of electrons and positrons is very small and the amount of energy released per electron is not enormously high. Still, Dirac's original theory of antiparticles was not confined to electrons. By his theory, any particle ought to have some corresponding antiparticle. Corresponding to the proton, for instance, there ought to be an *antiproton*. This would be just as massive as the proton and would carry a negative charge just as large as the proton's positive charge.

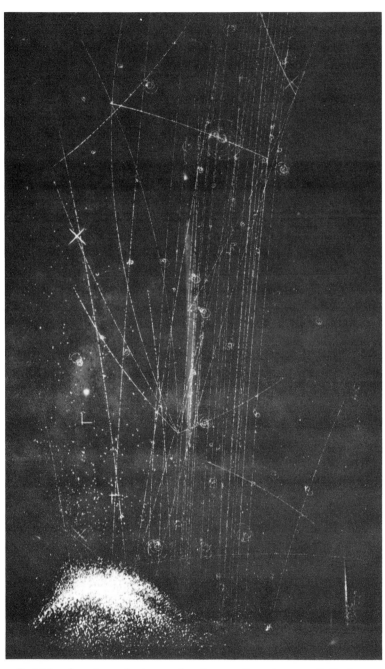

Bubble chamber photograph of an antiproton annihilation

An antiproton, however, is 1836 times as massive as a positron. It would take gamma rays or cosmic particles with 1836 times as much energy to form the proton-antiproton pair as would suffice for the electron-positron pair. Cosmic particles of the necessary energies existed but they were rare and the chance of someone being present with a particle detector just as a rare super-energetic cosmic particle happened to form a proton-antiproton pair was very small.

Physicists had to wait until they had succeeded in designing particle accelerators that would produce enough energy to allow the creation of proton-antiproton pairs. This came about in the early 1950s when a device called the *Cosmotron* was built at Brookhaven National Laboratory in Long Island in 1952 and another called the *Bevatron* at the University of California in Berkeley in 1954.

Using the Bevatron in 1956, Segrè (the discoverer of technetium who had, by that time, emigrated to the United States), the American physicist Owen Chamberlain, and others succeeded in detecting the antiproton.

The antiproton was as unlikely to last as long as the positron was. It was surrounded by myriads of proton-containing nuclei and in a tiny fraction of a second it would encounter one. The antiproton and the proton also underwent mutual annihilation, but having 1836 times the mass, they produced 1836 times the energy that was produced in the case of an electron and a positron.

There was even an *antineutron,* a particle reported in 1956 by the Italian-American physicist Oreste Piccioni and his co-workers. Since the neutron has no charge, the antineutron has no charge either, and one might wonder how the antineutron would differ from the neutron then. Actually, both have a small magnetic field. In the neutron the magnetic field is pointed in one direction with reference to the neutron's spin; in the antineutron it is pointed in the other.

In 1965 the American physicist Leon Max Lederman and his co-workers produced a combination of an antiproton and an antineutron that together formed an *antideuteron,* which is the nucleus of antihydrogen-2.

This is good enough to demonstrate that if antiparticles existed by themselves without the interfering presence of ordinary particles, they could form *antimatter*, which would be precisely identical with ordinary matter in every way except for the fact that electric charges and magnetic fields would be turned around. If antimatter were available to us, and if we could control the manner in which it united with matter, we would have a source of energy much greater and, perhaps, simpler to produce than would be involved in hydrogen fusion.

To be sure, there is no antimatter on earth, except for the submicroscopic amounts that are formed by the input of tremendous energies. Nor does anyone know of any conceivable way of forming antimatter at less energy than that produced by mutual annihilation, so that we might say that mankind can never make an energy profit out of it—except that with the memory of Rutherford's prediction that nuclear energy of any kind could never be tapped, one hesitates to be pessimistic about anything.

The Unknown

Physical theory makes it seem that particles and antiparticles ought to exist in the universe in equal quantities. Yet on earth (and, we can be quite certain, in the rest of the solar system and even, very likely, in the rest of the galaxy) protons, neutrons, and electrons are common, while antiprotons, antineutrons, and positrons are exceedingly rare.

Could it be that when the universe was first formed there were indeed equal quantities of particles and antiparticles but that they were somehow segregated, perhaps into galaxies and *antigalaxies?* If so, there might occasionally be collisions of a galaxy and an antigalaxy with the evolution of vast quantities of energy as mutual annihilation on a cosmic scale takes place.

There are, in fact, places in the heavens where radiation is unusually high in quantity and in energy. Can we be witnessing such enormous mutual annihilation?

Indeed, it is not altogether inconceivable that we may still have new types of forces and new sources of energy to discover. Until about 1900, no one suspected the existence of nuclear energy. Are we quite sure now that nuclear energy brings us to the end, and that there is not a form of energy more subtle still, and greater?

In 1962, for instance, certain puzzling objects called *quasars* were discovered far out in space, a billion light-years or more away from us. Each one shines from 10 to 100 times as brilliantly as an entire ordinary galaxy does, and yet may be no more than a hundred-thousandth as wide as a galaxy. This is something like finding an object 10 miles across that delivers as much total light as 100 suns.

It is very hard to understand where all that energy comes from and why it should be concentrated into so tiny a volume. Astronomers have tried to explain it in terms of the four interactions now known, but is it possible that there is a fifth greater than any of the four? If so, it is not impossible that eventually man's restless brain may come to understand and even utilize it.

APPENDIX

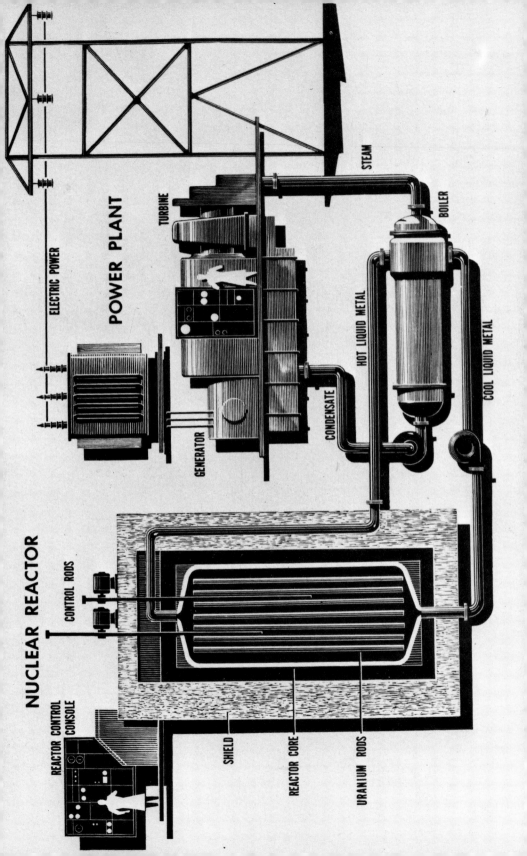

NUCLEAR REACTOR

POWER PLANT

REACTOR CONTROL CONSOLE

CONTROL RODS

SHIELD

REACTOR CORE

URANIUM RODS

TURBINE

GENERATOR

ELECTRIC POWER

CONDENSATE

HOT LIQUID METAL

COOL LIQUID METAL

STEAM

BOILER

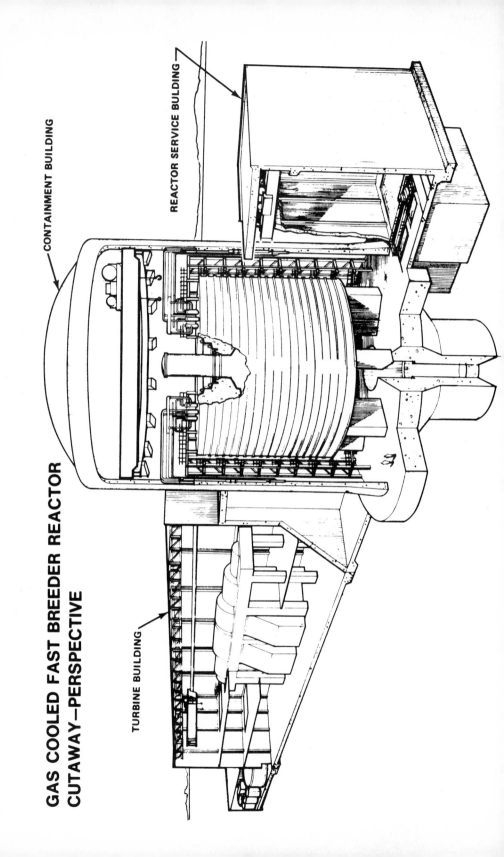

GAS COOLED FAST BREEDER REACTOR
CUTAWAY—PERSPECTIVE

CONTAINMENT BUILDING

REACTOR SERVICE BUILDING

TURBINE BUILDING

STURGIS
WORLD'S FIRST FLOATING NUCLEAR POWER STATION

1. REACTOR CONTAINMENT VESSEL
2. SPENT FUEL STORAGE TANK
3. PERSONNEL ACCESS DOOR
4. PRESSURIZER
5. CONTROL ROD DRIVE MECHANISMS
6. REACTOR
7. PRIMARY SHIELD TANK
8. PURGE SYSTEM
9. PRIMARY COOLANT LOOP
10. PRIMARY COOLANT PUMPS
11. STEAM GENERATOR
12. CONCRETE SHIELDING

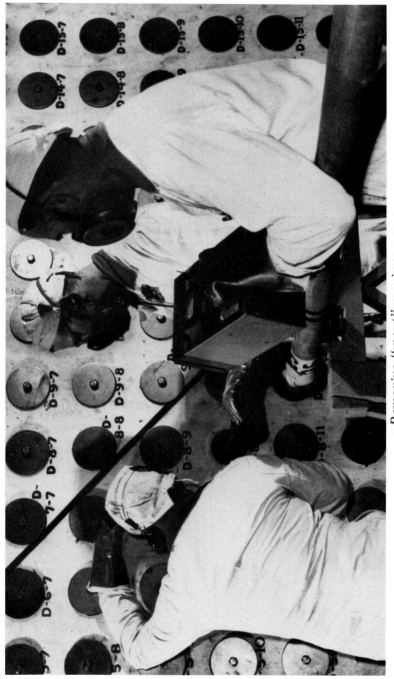

Removing "spent" uranium

800-ton nuclear furnace to supply steam for turbine-generator, before installation in 1968

Self-illuminated core while reactor is operating at full power

*Cooling canal pattern for four generating units on the coast of
South Florida as seen from 25,000 feet*

BIBLIOGRAPHY

For Young Students

Asimov, Isaac. *How Did We Find Out About Nuclear Power?* New York: Walker and Co., 1976.

————. *Inside the Atom.* New York: Abelard-Schuman, revised edition, 1974.

Blow, Michael. *The History of the Atomic Bomb.* New York: American Heritage Publishing Co., 1968.

Cline, Barbara Lovett. *The Questioners: Physicists and the Quantum Theory.* New York: Crowell Collier and Mac-Millan, 1965.

Curie, Eve. *Madame Curie: A Biography,* translated by Vincent Sheean. New York: Doubleday, 1937.

Dibner, Bern. *Wilhelm Roentgen and the Discovery of X Rays.* New York: Franklin Watts, 1968.

Einstein, Albert. *Relativity: The Special and General Theory,* translated by Robert W. Lawson. New York: Crown, 1961.

Ellis, R. Hobart, Jr. *Knowing the Atomic Nucleus.* New York: Lothrop, Lee and Shepard, 1973.

Esterer, Arnulf K. *Discoverer of X Rays: Wilhelm Conrad Roentgen.* New York: Julian Messner, 1968.

Faber, Doris. *Enrico Fermi: Atomic Pioneer*. Englewood Cliffs, N.J.: Prentice-Hall, 1966.

Frisch, Otto R. *Working with Atoms*. New York: Basic Books, 1965.

Gaines, Matthew. *Atomic Energy*. New York: Grosset & Dunlap, 1970.

Gamow, George. *Biography of Physics*. New York: Harper & Row, 1961.

Grey, Vivian. *Secret of the Mysterious Rays: The Discovery of Nuclear Energy*. New York: Basic Books, 1966.

Hughes, Donald. *The Neutron Story*. New York: Doubleday, 1956.

Kelman, Peter and A. Harris Stone. *Ernest Rutherford: Architect of the Atom*. Englewood Cliffs, N.J.: Prentice-Hall, 1969.

Lapp, Ralph E. *Roads to Discovery*. New York: Harper and Row, 1960.

McKown, Robin. *Giant of the Atom: Ernest Rutherford*. New York: Julian Messner, 1962.

Massey, Harrie S. W. and Arthur R. Quinton. *Basic Laws of Matter* (revised edition). Bronxville, N.Y.: Herald Books, 1965.

Romer, Alfred. *The Restless Atom*. New York: Doubleday, 1960.

Silverberg, Robert. *Men Who Mastered the Atom*. New York: G. P. Putnam's Sons, 1965.

————. *Niels Bohr: The Man Who Mapped the Atom*. Philadephia, Pa.: MacRae Smith, 1965.

General Reading

Amaldi, Ginestra. *The Nature of Matter: Physical Theory from Thales to Fermi*. Chicago: Chicago University Press, 1966.

Boorse, Henry A. and Lloyd Motz, eds. *The World of the Atom* (2 Vols.). New York: Basic Books, 1966.

Born, Max. *The Born-Einstein Letters: The Correspondence Between Albert Einstein and Max and Hedwig Born from 1916 to 1955,* translated by Irene Born. New York: Walker and Co., 1971.

Childs, Herbert. *An American Genius: The Life of Ernest Orlando*. New York: E. P. Dutton, 1968.

Compton, Arthur H. *Atomic Quest*. New York: Oxford University Press, 1956.

Einstein, Albert and Leopold Infeld. *The Evolution of Physics*. New York: Simon & Schuster, 1966.

Einstein, Albert. *Ideas and Opinions*. (revised ed.). New York: Dell, 1976.

Fermi, Laura. *Atoms in the Family: My Life with Enrico Fermi*. Chicago: University Press, 1954.

Frank, Philipp. *Einstein: His Life and Times*. New York: Alfred A. Knopf, 1953.

Gamow, George. *The Atom and Its Nucleus*. Englewood Cliffs, N.J.: Prentice-Hall, 1961.

Glasstone, Samuel. *Sourcebook on Atomic Energy* (third ed.). New York: Van Nostrand, 1967.

Greenaway, Frank. *John Dalton and the Atom*. Ithaca, N.Y.: Cornell University Press, 1966.

Hahn, Otto. *Otto Hahn: My Life,* translated by Ernest Kaiser and Eithne Wilkins. New York: Herder and Herder, 1970.

————. *Otto Hahn: A Scientific Autobiography,* edited and translated by Willy Ley. New York: Charles Scribner's Sons, 1966.

Heisenberg, Werner. *Physics and Beyond: Encounters and Conversations,* translated by Arthur J. Pomerans. New York: Harper and Row, 1970.

Kevles, Daniel J. *The Physicists: A History of a Scientific Community in Modern America*. New York: Knopf, 1978.

McCue, John J. G. *An Introduction to Physical Science: The World of Atoms* (second ed.). New York: The Ronald Press, 1963.

March, Robert H. *Physics for Poets*. New York: McGraw-Hill, 1970.

Michelmore, Peter. *The Swift Years: The Robert Oppenheimer Story*. New York: Dodd, Mead & Co., 1969.

Moore, Ruth. Niels Bohr: *The Man, His Science, and the World They Changed*. New York: Alfred A. Knopf, 1966.

Murphy, Arthur W., ed. *The Nuclear Power Controversy*. Englewood Cliffs, N.J.: Prentice-Hall, 1976.

Murray, Raymond L. *Nuclear Energy: An Introduction to the Concepts, Systems and Applications of Nuclear Processes*. New York: Pergamon Press, 1975.

Patterson, Elizabeth C. *John Dalton and the Atomic Theory: The Biography of a Natural Philosopher.* New York: Doubleday, 1970.

Patterson, Walter C. *Nuclear Power.* Harmondsworth, England: Penguin, 1976.

Rozental, S., ed. *Niels Bohr: His Life and Work as Seen by His Friends and Colleagues.* New York: John Wiley and Sons, 1967.

Schonland, Basil. *The Atomists (1805–1933).* New York: Oxford University Press, 1968.

Seaborg, Glenn T. *Man-made Transuranium Elements.* Englewood Cliffs, N.J.: Prentice-Hall, 1963.

Segrè, Emilio. *Enrico Fermi, Physicist.* Chicago: Chicago University Press, 1970.

Smyth, Henry D. *Atomic Energy for Military Purposes.* Princeton, N.J.: Princeton University Press, 1945.

Thirring, Hans. *Energy for Man: From Windmills to Nuclear Power.* New York: Harper Colophon Books, 1976.

Thomson, George. *J. J. Thomson: Discoverer of the Electron.* New York: Doubleday, 1966.

PHOTOGRAPH CREDITS

INDEX

Radioactivity, artificial, 69
Radiation, 21, 22
Ratcliffe, J. A., 30
Relativity, theory of, 54, 56, 63
Roentgen, Wilhelm Konrad, 19-21
Russell, Henry Norris, 118
Rutherford, Ernest, 23, 25-27, 30, 31, 48, 57, 59, 60, 65, 67, 73, 75, 77, 89, 95, 107. 119
Seaborg, Glenn Theodore, 95
Segrè, Emilio, 96, 132
Soddy, Frederick, 31, 32
Spizer, Lyman, Jr., 127
Stellarators, 127
Stoney, George Johnstone, 17
Strassman, Fritz, 97
Sun, 5, 6, 44, 45, 49, 53, 117-119, 122, 134
Supernova, 122
Szilard, Leo, 101, 102
Teller, Edward, 102
Thermal neutrons, 87, 88
Thermodynamics, the second law of, 48
Thermonuclear bomb, 119, 121, 122
Thermonuclear reactions, 6, 118
Thompson, Joseph John, 18, 20, 24, 25, 27, 34, 36, 59
Thorium, 22, 24, 29, 31, 32, 38, 48, 62
Ultraviolet light, 24

Uranium, 21, 22, 24, 29, 31, 32, 38, 46, 48, 49, 57, 61-64, 80, 89, 94, 96, 97, 103-105, 107, 110, 117
Urey, Harold Clayton, 37
von Helmholz, Hermann Ludwig Ferdinand, 40, 44, 45
von Weizsäcker, Carl Friedrich, 118
Walton, Ernest Thomas Sinton, 71
Ware, Alan Alfred, 127
Whewell, William, 25
X ray, 21, 28, 29, 83
Wigner, Eugene Paul, 102